EASY WAYS
to the PLANTS *of the*
BERNESE OBERLAND

EASY WAYS
to the PLANTS *of the*
BERNESE OBERLAND

SAWD
BOOKS

PHILIP AND JEAN TALBOYS

First published 1993 by SAWD Books, an imprint of SAWD Publications,
Plackett's Hole, Bicknor, Sittingbourne, Kent ME9 8BA

Design: Rachel Griffin
Map: Ian Moore

British Library Cataloguing-in-Publication Data
A catalogue record for this book is available from the British Library

ISBN: 1-872489-14-1

Printed and bound by
The Guernsey Press Company Limited, Vale, Guernsey, C.I.

To our friends in Switzerland

Walter Gigon, formerly President of
the Alpengarten Schynige Platte,
and his wife Marthe

Erwin and Rosemary Zingg-Dinkel of
Hotel Seiler au Lac, Bönigen

CONTENTS

COLOUR ILLUSTRATIONS

Plate 1 Plant Habitats in the Bernese Oberland
Fafleralp – alpine pastures below glacier
Gasterntal – glaciated valley from Stock cable car
Footpath from the Männlichen to Kleine Scheidegg
Sunnbühl – dry rocky grassland at foot of scree
Plate 2 The Alpengarten Schynige Platte
Meadow flowers in the alpine pasture
The acid beds
General view
Plate 3 Plants in the Alpengarten Schynige Platte
Primula auricula – auricula
Geum reptans – creeping avens
Thlaspi rotundifolium – round-leaved pennycress
Ranunculus parnassifolius – Parnassus-leaved buttercup
Plate 4 Plants in the Alpengarten Schynige Platte
Ranunculus glacialis – glacier crowfoot
Ranunculus seguieri – Séguier's buttercup
Viola biflora – yellow wood violet
Veronica aphylla – leafless-stemmed veronica
Plate 5 Snow-melt Plants
Soldanella alpina – alpine snowbell
Soldanella pusilla – least snowbell
Crocus albiflorus & Crocus vernus – white crocus & purple crocus
Ranunculus pyrenaeus – Pyrenean buttercup
Plate 6 Alpine Pasture Plants
Pulsatilla alpina – alpine pasque flower
Dactylorhiza sambucina – elder-flowered orchid
Pulsatilla alpina apiifolia – yellow alpine pasque flower
Pulsatilla vernalis – spring pasque flower
Plate 7 Alpine Pasture Orchids
Dactylorhiza majalis – broad-leaved marsh orchid
Gymnadenia conopsea – fragrant orchid
Platanthera bifolia – lesser butterfly orchid
Gymnadenia albida – small white orchid
Plate 8 Alpine Pasture Plants
Campanula thyrsoides – yellow bellflower
Pedicularis foliosa – leafy lousewort
Homogyne alpina – alpine coltsfoot
Pedicularis verticillata – verticillate lousewort
Plate 9 Alpine Pasture Plants
Primula farinosa – birdseye primrose
Lloydia serotina – Snowdon lily
Alchemilla alpina – alpine lady's mantle
Trifolium alpinum – alpine clover

Plate 10 Gentians
Gentiana punctata – spotted gentian
Gentiana brachyphylla – short-leaved gentian
Gentiana verna – spring gentian
Gentiana acaulis – trumpet gentian
Plate 11 Plants on Rocky Outcrops
Dryas octopetala – mountain avens
Androsace helvetica – Swiss rock-jasmine
Linaria alpina & Oxyria digyna – alpine toadflax & mountain sorrel
Globularia cordifolia – matted globularia
Plate 12 Plants on Rocky Outcrops
Sempervivum montanum – mountain houseleek
Veronica fruticans – rock speedwell
Silene acaulis – moss campion
Hutchinsia alpina – Chamois cress
Plate 13 Hay-meadow Plants
Paradisea liliastrum – St Bruno's lily
Lilium martagon – Martagon lily
Phyteuma orbiculare – round-headed rampion
Campanula barbata – bearded bellflower
Meadow plants including *Ligusticum mutellina, Geranium spp.*,
Leucanthemum vulgare – alpine lovage, cranesbill and ox-eye daisy
Phyteuma spicatum – spiked rampion
Plate 14 Tall Herbaceous Plants
Aconitum vulparia – wolfsbane
Astrantia major – great masterwort
Swertia perennis – marsh felwort
Thalictrum aquilegifolium – great meadow-rue
Plate 15 Plants Growing in Damp Conditions
Trollius europaeus – globeflower
Anemone narcissiflora – narcissus-flowered anemone
Pinguicula alpina – alpine butterwort
Gagea fistulosa – gagea
Cypripedium calceolus – lady's slipper orchid
Saxifraga aizoides – yellow mountain saxifrage
Plate 16 Alpine Shrubs
Loiseleuria procumbens & Vaccinium myrtillus
– creeping azalea & bilberry or whortleberry
Rhododendron ferrugineum – alpenrose
Vaccinium myrtillus – bilberry or whortleberry
Salix reticulata – netted willow
Polygala chamaebuxus – shrubby milkwort
Clematis alpina – alpine clematis

COVER Heart of the Bernese Oberland: Eiger, Mönch and Jungfrau and
the Männlichen from Schynige Platte.
Leontopodium alpinum – edelweiss, *Gentiana acaulis* – trumpet gentian.

1
Easy Ways

During a series of visits to the Bernese Oberland in late June or early July, from 1981 to 1992, we have found easy ways to travel from Interlaken into the mountains using public transport. We are retired professional horticulturalists, and although appreciably limited by physical disability, one a chronic asthmatic and the other arthritic, we have been able to visit numerous interesting and beautiful places without undue physical effort. We hope that this account of our travels will encourage others to experience the 'Alpine Spring' at first hand – 'The Easy Way'. However it is most important that anyone who has either respiratory or cardio-vascular problems should consult their doctor before attempting to undertake the excursions we describe.

There are full travel details for 26 excursions giving maximum altitude, and a list of plants likely to be found in each locality. The book, which contains over 60 full-colour illustrations of plants, has been based on our large collection of photographs taken in the Bernese Oberland over a number of seasons. The collection only contains slides of good specimens, found in reasonable weather conditions for photography, and does not contain all the plants in the Bernese Oberland. If we do not mention a particular plant, in a particular place, it does not mean it never grows there, but merely that we have not been there on the right day; you may find it on your first visit! There is a wide seasonal variation in both the number of flowers and date of flowering of the same species in the same place, so the lists of plants that we suggest that you might find in a particular location should only be treated as an indication of what you are likely to find, for there is no certainty in these matters; grazing animals may have been there before you!

On some of the excursions we have suggested extended walks for those who are reasonably fit; in many cases they have been explored by the younger members of our own family, but we have not been able to try them ourselves, and thus have no photographs or plant records.

How to use this book

Before choosing an excursion you can find information on:

    Alpine Plants – Chapter 3 (p.14)

    Books for Identifying Plants (p.4)

    Clothing and Equipment – Chapter 2 (p.12)

                        Chapter 6 (p.48)

    Maps – Chapter 2 (p.12)

    Plant Photography – Equipment – Chapter 4 (p.21)

    Provisions – Chapter 6 (p.48)

    Tickets and Tourist Concessions – Chapter 4 (p.6)

    Timetables – Chapter 4 (p.6-7)

    Travel facilities – Chapter 2 (p.5)

Learning Names of Alpine Plants

    Read – Alpengarten Schynige Platte – Chapter 6 (p.28)

    Use – Books listed (p.4)

    Visit – Alpengarten Schynige Platte - Excursion 1 (p.49)

Going on an excursion – Take this book with you
Chapter 6 contains details of 26 Excursions.
Altitudes
Map (p.46-47)
Plants likely to be seen.
Scenery
Towns and Villages
Travel

Chapter 7 Index (p.94-97) will help you find information on

Photography
    equipment
    films
    techniques
Places
    altitude
    excursions
    local details
Plants
    characteristics of alpines
    English names
    illustrations
    photographic techniques
    scientific names

Travel
    boats
    buses
    cable-cars
    chair-lifts
    funiculars
    gondolas
    maps
    mountain-railways
    post-buses
    tickets
    time-tables
    tourist concessions
    trains
    vocabulary

USEFUL BOOKS FOR PLANT IDENTIFICATION

The Alpine Flowers of Britain and Europe
by Christopher Grey-Wilson and Marjorie Blamey
published by Collins & Sons, London.

Our Alpine Flora
by Elias Landolt translated by Krystyna Urbanska
published by the Swiss Alpine Club.

Collins Guide to the Grasses, Sedges, Rushes and Ferns of Britain and Northern Europe
by Richard Fitter, Alastair Fitter and Ann Farrer
published by Collins & Sons, London.

The Wild Flowers of Britain and Northern Europe
by Richard Fitter, Alastair Fitter and Marjorie Blamey
published by Collins & Sons, London.

We cannot end this brief introduction to the Easy Ways to the Plants of the Bernese Oberland without acknowledging the kindness of our Swiss friends.

We are particularly grateful to Dr Walter Gigon, formerly President of the Alpengarten Schynige Platte, for his unfailing help and encouragement throughout the production of this book. Both he and the staff of the Garden, have patiently answered our many questions and kindly provided us with information, including the plan of the Alpengarten used as Fig 1.

We must also thank our many friends at the Hotel Seiler au Lac, Bönigen, where our family has always enjoyed Swiss hospitality at its very best. The Seiler has given us more than a home from home and quietly provided everything that was required to make each of our many visits a truly memorable occasion.

4

TRAVEL *in the* BERNESE OBERLAND

INTERLAKEN – AN EXCELLENT TRAVEL CENTRE

All the excursions described in chapter 6 start from Interlaken which is the centre of an excellent transport network providing easy travel throughout the Bernese Oberland. The schedules for all forms of transport are carefully co-ordinated and you can rely on getting to your planned destination on time, so that you can embark on quite complicated journeys and feel confident that you will achieve your objective and return home in time for your evening meal.

The discount arrangements that are available for tourists make it possible to reach quite remote areas very cheaply using the reliable combined services provided by a number of railway companies, buses, post-buses and lake steamers.

There are two railway stations, Interlaken Ost and Interlaken West, and two associated quays for the boats providing regular services to the lakeside towns and villages, Interlaken Ost for Brienzersee, and Interlaken West for Thunersee. The river Aare flows through Interlaken from Brienzersee to Thunersee but navigation is not possible between the lakes as there are sluice gates controlling the water-levels. The terminus for most buses and post-buses is outside Interlaken West railway station. Practically all the staff employed on any form of transport speak English, so buying your ticket and confirming that you are in the right place at the right time is very easy. Most public notices are in German, but stations and tourist offices offer a wide range of illustrated tourist's leaflets, including maps and travel details, with local information in German, French and English.

Most mountain travellers make an early start, shops are often open at 07.00 or 07.30 so it is easy to buy provisions and make the most of a fine day. The weather in the high mountains frequently deteriorates during the afternoon, mist and low cloud descend, rapidly reducing visibility with a very marked drop in temperature. Most mountain railways, funiculars, cable-cars, gondelbahns and chair-lifts start running early in the day and close between 17.00 and 18.00. Some close for an hour sometime between 12.00 and 14.00 so it is well to complete your outward journey before noon.

TICKETS – BILLETT

You can usually buy a 'through ticket' for your journey from Interlaken railway station even if you are going to make a number of changes en route and use a combination of trains, buses, post-buses, boats and funiculars etc. The booking offices tend to be very busy early in the morning so allow plenty of time to get your tickets. The staff are invariably helpful and sell tickets for buses and post-buses. If you travel by train between two lakeside villages or towns you can make the return trip by boat.

REGIONAL PASSES

A 15-day Bernese Oberland Regional Pass in 1992 cost S.Fr.125 (£50 approx) and provided free travel (with minor exceptions) on any five days within the specified area of the Bernese Oberland; and half-price travel within this area on the other 10 days. Charges for journeys beyond this area are discounted at 50% or 25% on all 15 days. Most of the excursions suggested in this book can be completed without any additional charges on a 'free-day', so it is possible to save the cost of the pass on one or two journeys. The passes are available from tourist offices, tour couriers or railway stations and are valid on trains, buses, post-buses, boats and mountain railways. They also cover charges on some cable-cars, gondolas, funiculars and chair-lifts, but on others 50% or 25% discounts are offered and there are no 'free-day' concessions. If you are on a 'free-day' you do not need to buy a ticket, unless you plan to go beyond the region; if you are going to need additional tickets, you will be able to buy these at Interlaken before you start on your journey.

A Regional Pass and a Timetable (Fahrplan) are the most important items to obtain before planning an excursion in the Bernese Oberland.

THE MAIN-LINE & INTER-CITY RAILWAYS

The Swiss railways are run by a number of companies and the rolling-stock carries the appropriate logo which is also shown on the timetable. The engines are large and impressive, hauling inter-city trains across Europe. At the station (Bahnhof) you will usually find a list showing the platform or track (gleis) for each train. Many trains are long and may divide at various points so check the nameboard on the outside of the coach to make sure you are going to the right destination.

Express trains, stopping only at large towns, are known as 'Schnellzug' and local trains stopping at most stations are 'Regionalzug'. Often trains of each type run to the same destinations within a few minutes of each other from the same platform so you need to make sure you are using the right one; the Schnellzug may not stop where you are hoping to go and the Regionalzug may be too late for your planned connection! Most of the main-line trains have a trolley refreshment service.

BUSES

There are bus services in and around Interlaken, Thun and Brienz and their surrounding villages.

POST-BUSES

The postal services are taken to many outlying areas by distinctive bright yellow post-buses which carry passengers and run to a very strict timetable. They all carry a post-horn symbol and give warning of their approach around steep, blind hairpin bends by a loud electronic post-horn call.

MOUNTAIN RAILWAYS

Trains on rack-and-pinion railways can ascend steep slopes by zig-zagging up the mountain-side and transport a large number of passengers and a substantial weight of freight to a considerable height. Most are electrically powered but the Brienzer Rothorn Bahn still uses a number of coal-fired steam locomotives. Progress is leisurely, along single tracks, giving ample time to enjoy the scenery and plants, with frequent stops at points to allow trains going in the other direction to pass. Passenger accommodation is often fairly basic, with wooden slatted seats. It is often more comfortable to travel facing uphill to avoid having to constantly brace oneself to avoid slipping off the seat!

FUNICULAR RAILWAYS – SEILBAHNEN

Funiculars run on rails but are driven by cables winding over drums. There is a rack-and-pinion locking mechanism to hold the vehicle in the unlikely event of cable failure. The vehicles and 'station platforms' are constructed stepwise to conform to the very steep inclines for which they are designed. The vehicles normally run in pairs, one going up as the other goes down on straight tracks. Some very long funiculars operate in two stages so that the track can change direction at a mid-way station where passengers move to another vehicle for the second part of their journey. The seats remain flat but some people find the downhill view rather unnerving and prefer to concentrate on the plants on either side of the track!

CABLE-CARS – LUFTSEILBAHNEN

Cable-cars are enclosed vehicles suspended on cables carried on pylons taking passengers and freight to great heights very speedily. Although some travel across dramatic spaces, many simply glide effortlessly just above the tree tops and all provide fascinating viewpoints of the ground beneath. Cable-cars may carry 20 people or more, most of whom have to stand throughout their journey, but smaller gondolas carrying 2, 4 or 6 seated passengers also operate on cables, running continuously up and down the mountain. They are disconnected briefly from the cable to allow passengers to enter and alight, and staff are always available to assist less mobile travellers. On some of the gondelbahns there are intermediate stations where you can alight if you wish to explore at an intermediate level, but most people prefer to be carried to the top of the mountain. Passing through such an intermediate station can be surprising at first; there are often sudden changes of direction and a rapid acceleration as you leave the station.

CHAIR-LIFTS – SESSELBAHNEN

Chair-lifts are also carried on continuous moving cables supported on pylons, generally 20-30ft above the ground, and often sited amongst coniferous trees. Passengers are seated individually or in pairs, facing either forwards or sideways, and are kept secure by a bar which hinges down in front at the level of the arm rests. A hook is provided to hold bags and rucksacks safely. Staff are always at hand to help passengers mount and dismount and help with baggage, and often will supply large warm coats, free of charge, to wear on the journey. Always accept this extra protection if it is offered as they will know if the weather is colder further up the mountain. Chair-lifts rise to substantial heights, and sitting under such exposed conditions can be a cold experience, and it is practically impossible to put on extra clothing once you are securely fixed behind the restraining bar. The smooth and almost silent motion, and unusual 'bird's eye' view of the terrain beneath soon dissipates any initial apprehension in the more 'trepid' traveller. As with cable-cars and gondolas, passage through intermediate stations may be a little disconcerting.

FOOTPATHS – WANDERWEGE, BERGWEGE AND PANORAMAWEGE

Public transport in Switzerland is closely geared to the requirements of walkers: most destinations, by whatever means of access, are starting-points for lengthy and energetic walks. As could be expected, there is a comprehensive system of footpaths, all extensively way-marked. Sign posts point the way and indicate the distance, but not in kilometres, instead they show the time taken to walk to the various destinations, in hours, (std = stunde) and minutes (min). It is important to bear in mind that these times assume steady and continuous walking at a speed of 4.2km/hr on the level; they do not allow for stopping to identify and photograph numerous plants, nor do they make any allowance for those with some physical impairment.

The signposts also show a two-category classification of the footpaths: Wanderwege provide relatively easy walking conditions, requiring only strong walking shoes. They are indicated by plain yellow arrows. Bergwege are suitable only for experienced mountain walkers, and require strong boots with non-slip soles. They are indicated by red-and-white arrows. The walks detailed in this book are mostly on Wanderwege. Weatherproof clothing and adequate protection from sunburn should be carried on all walking excursions in the mountains; the weather can change very rapidly. Panoramawege are footpaths that provide spectacular views of the mountain scenery.

MAPS

Forward planning, using maps showing clear contours, is important when making excursions into the mountains, even if public transport is readily available. It is especially important if any members of the group have physical impairments that limit their capacity to keep up with the more vigorous members or have difficulty in walking uphill at higher altitudes. The following maps are suggested for excursions mentioned in this book.

Scale of 1:50,000

(Comparable with O.S. Landranger Series in UK, 2cm:1km 1.25in:1 mile.)

Landeskarte der Schweiz 1:50,000: Berner Oberland, 5004

A good overall view, and useful for planning, but the footpaths are not easy to read in the field.

Landeskarte der Schweiz 1:50,000: Offizielle Wanderkarte der SAW

Excellent maps for walkers, with footpaths in red and post-bus routes in yellow, but each covers a rather limited area (35x24km) and they are not yet available for all parts of Switzerland.

253T(Gantrisch), 254T(Interlaken), 263T(Wildstrubel) and *264T(Jungfrau)* cover most of the excursions listed in chapter 6.

Kummerly & Frey: - *Wanderkarte Berner Oberland Ost*
                       - *Wanderkarte Berner Oberland West*

Very good for field use, although rather large. Footpaths are in red, post-bus routes in blue, and nature reserves outlined with a broad red band.

Scale of 1:25,000

(Comparable with O.S. Pathfinder Series in UK, 4cm:1km 2.5in:1 mile.)

Landeskarte der Schweiz: 1:25,000

Large-scale maps, but each covering only a very small area (18x12km). They are invaluable as an aid to planning for the less active walker because footpaths can be examined in detail in relation to contours to assess the extent of 'ups and downs'. Although footpaths are marked in black they are clear enough to be usable in the field

1209(Brienz), 1227(Niesen), 1228(Lauterbrunnen),
1229(Grindelwald), 1247(Adelboden), 1248(Mürren),
1268(Lötschental) cover most of the excursions listed in chapter 6.

The 1:50,000 and 1:25,000 maps look very much like the corresponding series in the UK and this can lead to a misunderstanding of the heights indicated by contour line intervals on the Swiss maps. The vertical distance between successive contour lines on UK Landranger maps for the south of England is 10m, whereas on the corresponding 1:50,000 Swiss map it is 20m. Similarly the UK Pathfinder maps have a vertical interval of 5m but for the Swiss 1:25,000 it is 20m - four times the height for a similar horizontal distance!

3
ALPINE PLANTS

Our title refers to 'Plants of the Bernese Oberland' because we shall discuss plants that occur on mountains but are not generally regarded as 'Alpines', as well as many that are. But what are 'Alpines'? The horticultural definition according to the Royal Horticultural Society and Alpine Garden Society is 'any plant suitable to be grown in a rock-garden or an unheated alpine-house or frame.' i.e. a plant that is small and hardy under conditions in the UK and not necessarily of mountain origin although many are. For the authors of alpine floras it is convenient to include all plants growing above a particular altitude, e.g. Grey-Wilson and Blamey, in 'Alpine Flowers of Britain and Europe' use 1000m as the defining altitude; Landolt and Urbanska, in 'Our Alpine Flora' (i.e. of Switzerland) use 1500m. A specified altitude is acceptable when considering plants of a fairly limited area, and better if it corresponds with some ecological boundary, or one that is easily recognised in the field.

Probably the most satisfactory definition of an 'alpine plant' is one that occurs predominantly above the tree-line. Although the altitude of the tree-line varies greatly in different parts of the world, it always marks the physiological limit of altitude for tree growth and is therefore comparable world-wide. This is the definition we are using here, but within the Bernese Oberland there are many interesting and beautiful plants that occur predominantly below the tree-line, but are no less worthy of our attention.

The Bernese Oberland ranges in altitude from about 560m(1,837ft) at Interlaken on the shores of the Brienzersee and the Thunersee, to 4,158m(13,642ft) at the summit of the Jungfrau which, with the Eiger, 3,970m(13,026ft), and the Mönch, 4,099m(13,449ft), dominates the region. The Finsteraarhorn is even higher, 4,273m(14,020ft), but is more remote and is concealed behind the 'front-row' of the Jungfrau group. Public transport reaches its highest level at the Jungfraujoch, 3,456m(11,333ft), which is the highest railway station in Europe.

Air temperatures fall with increasing altitude, on average by 0.5°C for every 100m(328ft), but ranging from 0.7°C in spring and summer to 0.4°C in autumn and winter. In early summer the temperature difference between Interlaken and the Jungfraujoch can be 20°C/36°F. Even the Niesen, 2,362m(7,750ft), may be 12° or 13°C cooler than Interlaken, and in the strong winds that often prevail at high altitudes the additional 'wind chill' factor can be considerable.

For plant-life the temperature differences with altitude have important effects on the kinds of vegetation encountered in the mountains. Factors increasing with altitude include rainfall, increasing on average by 100mm per 100m altitude between 500m and 2500m; amount and duration of snow cover; wind speeds; and intensity of solar radiation, leading to heating of rocks etc. Reduced atmospheric pressure and temperature cause reduced humidity and increased drying.

Weathering of rocks by extremes of temperature, rainfall etc at the higher levels results in fragments ranging from boulders to soil-sized particles, all tending to move downwards until trapped in hollows or arrested on level ground. 'Soil' that accumulates is low in nutrients until substantial vegetation has developed and become incorporated, as humus, enabling soil and scree to become stabilised by plant growth. The nature of the underlying rock largely determines the acidity and calcium content of the soil, although conditions affecting the breakdown of plant debris and its incorporation in mineral material can also influence the acidity of the surface layers.

Weather conditions and the availability of soil are reflected in the zoning of vegetation on mountain slopes. On most high mountains there are 3 or 4 zones with more or less clearly defined boundaries: on the lower slopes and in the valleys the land is predominantly used for farming. As the slope increases, farm-land gives way to forest, with clearings where the slope is manageable for hay or cattle. With increasing altitude, beech and mixed forest give way to coniferous trees. There comes a point, however, at which lack of soil, low temperature and high winds suppress tree growth. The limit of tree-growth – the 'tree-line' is often very clearly defined. Higher up, equally clearly defined, is the 'snow-line', the level above which snow and ice persist throughout the summer. Between the tree-line and the snow-line is the alpine zone, characterised by low shrubby vegetation and short wiry grasses, with outcrops of rocks, screes etc. It is in this zone that alpine plants flourish. Some even occur above the snow-line, in crevices or under overhanging rocks, or on ridges where snow cannot settle or is soon blown away.

The definition of an 'alpine' as 'any plant growing predominantly above the tree-line' provides a useful grouping of plants from similar locations in different parts of the world, wherever the altitude is great enough to cause tree-growth to be suppressed by low temperatures and other altitude-related factors.

16

The altitude of both tree-line and snow-line depends on the latitude of the mountains. At the equator the tree-line is at about 3,000-3,500m(10,000-11,500ft); in the European Alps it is between 1,500m and 2,000m(5,000 and 7,000ft); in extreme northern Europe beyond the arctic circle, the tree-line is effectively at sea level, for in this region the altitude limit of tree growth coincides with the northern limit of forests, and the alpine flora merges with the arctic flora, the two floras having a number of plants in common, e.g. *Androsace chamaejasme* (ciliate rock-jasmine), *Bartsia alpina* (alpine bartsia), *Dryas octopetala* (mountain avens) [Pl.11], *Silene acaulis* (moss campion) [Pl.12], *Polygonum viviparum* (alpine bistort), *Ranunculus glacialis* (glacier crowfoot) [Pl.4], *Saxifraga aizoides* (yellow mountain saxifrage) [Pl.15], *Loiseleuria procumbens* (creeping azalea) [Pl.16] and *Rhodiola rosea* (roseroot). At these high latitudes the farming and forest zones are no longer represented.

As well as varying with latitude, the tree-line varies within each mountain region. It is modified by local conditions, and is commonly higher on the south side of a range than on the north side, in the northern hemisphere.

One of the apparent hazards faced by alpine plants is a long winter under the snow, but in fact a thick blanket of snow provides excellent protection against the extremely low air temperatures prevailing in the winter. Plants buried under 50cm of snow will generally be refrigerated at -1 to -2°C. Under these conditions the plants are effectively 'dry' because water is only present as ice, but they do not become desiccated because there is no air movement around them. The snow surrounding them may not finally melt until mid-June or later in the Bernese Oberland. They emerge into full summer sunshine, well supplied with melt water. It is a feature of the alpine spring that a great flush of flowering takes place within a period of less than a month, led by crocuses, soldanellas, globularias, gentians and primulas. Urgency is necessary because vegetative growth, flowering and seeding must be completed before the snow returns for another winter. The snow-free period is short, and decreases with increasing altitude. In the Alps the 'growing season' is about 8 months at 1,000m(3,280ft) and decreases by about 10 days per 100m(328ft) increase in altitude, to 2 months at 2,500m(8,200ft). Flowering plants mostly need at least 2 months to complete their active cycle. The 'retreat' of the snow up the mountains in June and July makes it possible to experience the alpine spring over several weeks by moving to progressively higher altitudes.

Some alpines grow in places that are not protected by snow, e.g. on ridges where any snow is soon blown away. Such plants e.g. *Loiseleuria procumbens* (creeping azalea) [Pl.16] can survive extremely low temperatures as well as the desiccating and mechanically damaging effects of strong winds. Desiccation is a hazard for many alpines, where soil is thin or non-existent, and water drains away rapidly, or may be frozen. They combat this hazard in several ways that are comparable with those of plants in hot arid climates: Hairy or woolly shoots e.g. *Leontopodium alpinum* (edelweiss) [cover], or leaves with woolly undersides e.g. *Dryas octopetala* (mountain avens) [Pl.11], *Rhododendron ferrugineum* (alpenrose) [Pl.16], *Salix reticulata* (netted willow) [Pl.16] or leaves with margins rolled under to enclose stomata e.g. *Carex fuliginosa* (syn. *Carex ferruginea*) (red-brown sedge). Some plants have thick waxy cuticles to reduce water loss and fleshy stems and leaves for water storage, e.g. *Sempervivum montanum* (mountain houseleek) [Pl.12] and some saxifrages.

Alpine plants are characteristically low-growing, and

often in the form of mats, rosettes or cushions. The 'low profile' gives them the advantage of the 'boundary layer' effect i.e. the marked reduction in wind speed of air moving in contact with a surface. The effect is enhanced if the surface is rough, and the habit of growing amongst short wiry grass is common amongst alpines. Some grow closely pressed to rock surfaces, and send long roots deep into crevices or screes towards sources of water and giving anchorage, e.g. dwarf willows. Where there is only a thin layer of soil over the underlying rock, the grasses and sedges become increasingly sparse, and natural 'rock-gardens' become a feature, with various species forming colourful associations, such as *Dryas octopetala* (mountain avens), *Globularia cordifolia* (matted globularia) and *Silene acaulis* (moss campion).

Of all alpines, those most admired by enthusiasts are the 'cushion types', forming hemispherical masses of closely packed shoots adhering to rock surfaces, often with the whole plant surface covered with flowers e.g. *Androsace helvetica* (blunt-leaved rock-jasmine) [Pl.11]. This structure gives a stream-lined form, minimising wind damage and at the same time the close packing reduces water loss from the individual shoots. A similar packing of shoots but in a mat rather than a cushion, is shown by *Silene acaulis* (moss campion) [Pl.12].

The flowers of alpines are generally white or brightly coloured, and often large in relation to the whole plant. Most are insect-pollinated, but some such as the dwarf willows, are wind-pollinated.

The flowers of the alpine zone are the ones which attract most attention, but the hay meadows [Pl.13] at lower altitudes can give equal pleasure early in the season, with their enormous variety of herbaceous plants, including campanulas, clovers, campions, geraniums, knapweeds, lovage, rampions, and *Veratrum album* (white false helleborine) etc.

At the lowest levels the hay meadows may have already been cut by the time the snow has melted above the tree-line, but some higher meadows will still be at their most colourful. There is great variety in the predominant species present in the meadows, even within the same locality.

CONSERVATION

Switzerland has strict regulations for the conservation of wild plants. In nature reserves all picking and digging of any plant is prohibited. Elsewhere numerous plants are under total or partial protection. Partial protection usually prohibits both digging out and cutting more than a specified number of stems, usually either 3-5 stems or 10. However the rules are complicated and may vary from one Canton to another. In practice the sensible course of action is never to dig or cut any alpine plant. Taking photographs is permissible, but take great care to avoid trampling the vegetation in the vicinity.

For more detailed information on particular alpine species, see *Our Alpine Flora* by E. Landolt & *K.M. Urbanska, 1989, Swiss Alpine Club*. This includes information on the conservation status of individual species.

For general information, and identification of Swiss alpines, see *The Alpine Flowers of Britain and Europe* by C. Grey-Wilson & Marjorie Blamey.

4
PHOTOGRAPHING PLANTS

Alpine flowers are irresistible subjects for photography, but the results of holiday photographs are often disappointing. The aim of this chapter is to help the inexperienced photographer to produce acceptable pictures: it is not written by a photographic expert, but by someone with long experience of a limited range of equipment which has yielded all the photographs reproduced in this book.

THE CAMERA

The main requirement is to be able to take carefully focused photographs at close range. A single lens reflex (SLR) camera taking 35mm film is the most convenient option, preferably with through-the-lens (TTL) metering and the alternative of automatic or manual shutter-speed operation, with 'aperture priority'. This means that the aperture (f-number) is set at the required value (see page 22) and the camera will compute the necessary shutter-speed to give the correct exposure. The great advantage of the SLR is that the image seen in the view finder is exactly the same as that which will appear on the film. The camera used for the photographs in this book was a

Minolta X-700, but comparable models are available from Nikon, Olympus, Canon, Pentax etc.

The standard 50mm lens supplied with most 35mm cameras can be used satisfactorily for many flower photographs, focusing down to about 35cm from the subject, but an even closer approach is needed for very small flowers, and is available with lenses having a so-called 'Macro facility'. A Tamron 90mm lens with a Minolta mount was used for most of our photographs. It will focus down to 22cm from the front of the lens, and at that distance the image on the film is half the size of the subject. At a much higher cost, macro-lenses can be obtained giving a 1:1 ratio of image to subject, or more. The focusing ring on each lens shows distances in metres and feet. Incidentally, for flower 'portraits' it is usually best to ensure that stigma and stamens are sharply focused, if they are visible, for they carry much of the 'character' of the flower, as do the eyes in a human or animal 'sitter'.

'ALL THOSE PECULIAR NUMBERS' EXPLAINED

To obtain a satisfactory photograph a carefully controlled amount of light has to pass through the camera lens and to strike the sensitive film at the back of the camera. The amount of light reaching the film depends on two things: the size of the variable aperture in the camera's diaphragm, which can be set on a scale, and on the length of time the shutter remains open, i.e. the shutter speed.

Apertures are numbered as a series of 'f' numbers or 'stops':

22 16 11 8 5.6 4 2.8 1.7

22

Gasterntal
– glaciated valley from Stock cablecar

Fafleralp
– alpine pastures below glacier

Footpath from the Männlichen
to Kleine Scheidegg

Sunnbühl
– dry rocky grassland at foot of scree

Plate 1

Meadow flowers in the alpine pasture   The acid beds

General view

Plate 2

Geum reptans – creeping avens

Primula auricula
– auricula

Thlaspi rotundifolium
– round-leaved pennycress

Ranunculus parnassifolius – Parnassus-leaved buttercup

Plate 3

Ranunculus glacialis
– glacier crowfoot

Ranunculus seguieri
– Séguier's buttercup

(above) Viola biflora
– yellow wood violet

(below)Veronica aphylla
– leafless-stemmed veronica

Plate 4

Soldanella alpina – alpine snowbell

…danella pusilla
…ast snowbell

Crocus albiflorus & Crocus vernus
– white crocus & purple crocus

…nunculus pyrenaeus – Pyrenean buttercup

Plate 5

Pulsatilla alpina
– alpine pasque flower

Dactylorhiza sambucina
– elder-flowered orchid

Pulsatilla alpina apiifolia
– yellow alpine pasque flower

Pulsatilla vernalis
– spring pasque flower

Plate 6

ctylorhiza majalis
road-leaved marsh orchid

Gymnadenia conopsea
– fragrant orchid

tanthera bifolia
esser butterfly orchid

Gymnadenia albida
– small white orchid

Plate 7

Campanula thyrsoides
– yellow bellflower

Pedicularis foliosa
– leafy lousewort

Homogyne alpina
– alpine coltsfoot

Pedicularis verticillata
– verticillate lousewort

Plate 8

The largest number is the smallest aperture, and each successive number represents a doubling of the area of the opening, and thus a doubling of the amount of light passing through.

Shutter speeds are numbered in a series representing fractions of a second, thus:

1000 500 250 125 60 30 15 8 4 2 1

The largest number is the shortest exposure (1/1000sec) and each successive value doubles the exposure.

Film ratings also are numbers in a 'doubling' series:

25 50(or 64) 100 200 400 ISO (or ASA) units

A film rate of 25 ISO units is a very slow one, 400 ISO is a fast one. A doubling of the the film rating enables the exposure to be halved or the aperture to be reduced by 1 stop.

Suppose for example, that a camera is loaded with 100 ISO film, and that to photograph a particular scene at an aperture of f8 the meter shows that a shutter speed of 1/60sec is required. Other things being equal, the same scene could also be shot at 1/15sec at f16, or 1/30sec at f11, or 1/250sec at f4. All would be a correct exposure; but other things are not equal! The aperture affects not only the amount of light entering the camera, but also the depth of focus of the image; and the shutter speed affects not only the duration of exposure, but also the consequences of movement, both of the camera and of the subject. All of these are important in plant photography up a mountain.

Depth of focus also varies with the focal length of the lens, being large with a short-focus (wide-angle) lens and small with a long-focus (telephoto) lens. By using a wide-angle lens (c.28mm) at a small aperture (f22 or f16) it is possible to photograph plants in the near foreground with a distant view of the mountains etc in the background.

For 'documentary' work, aiming to record the appearance of a plant as precisely as possible, a large depth of focus is generally essential, to ensure that important parts of the plant do not simply fade into a blurred image. In 'close-ups' of *Pinguicula alpina,* for example, it is often difficult to ensure that both flowers and leaves are sharply in focus. To achieve a large depth of focus requires a small aperture, f16 or f22. In the example above, this would require 1/15 or 1/8sec exposures, respectively, and even longer under dull conditions. The problem then is to hold the camera steady for the relatively long exposures, while waiting for the wind to drop and the plant to stand still. A blurred image will result from movement of the camera or the subject. A camera support is therefore essential (see below), ideally a tripod, and a cable release to avoid jerky movement when the shutter is operated.

A further possibility would be to use a faster film. With 400 ISO film instead of the 100 ISO film in the example above, the exposure would be 1/250sec at f8, 1/60sec at f16, 1/500sec at f5.6, and 1/1000sec at f4. The latter speeds would be enough to 'freeze' some movement of the camera or the subject. Again, there are two problems: under very bright conditions the fastest shutter speed may be too slow; and faster films tend to be more coarsely grained than slow ones, although this is becoming less of a problem with modern films.

CAMERA SUPPORT

Although a tripod is the best form of support it can be weighty and bulky to use in the mountains. A valuable alternative is a monopod, a one-legged support that will extend to eye-level or retract to c.45cm, with a ball-and-socket attachment for the camera. The photographer, feet apart, provides two other legs to form, in effect, a tripod, which can be surprisingly stable. Retracted, it can be used whilst kneeling on the ground. When not in use for photography it can be used as a walking stick.

If a small tripod is being used for close-ups of very small plants, it is convenient to use a right-angled viewer attached to the view-finder to avoid having to become a contortionist to apply an eye to the normal view-finder when it is near ground-level. Once the camera is fixed and focused one can sit and wait for suitable conditions without necessarily looking through the view-finder; but remember to cover the eye-piece whilst operating the shutter, otherwise extraneous light entering through the view-finder can result in serious under-exposure.

LIGHTING

It has been said that the amateur photographer is always waiting for the sun to come out, whereas the professional is always waiting for it to go in! It is not always appreciated that much better rendering of colour can be obtained under dull conditions, or even in rain (if someone holds an umbrella over the camera!) than in bright sunlight. Direct sunlight can result in colours being 'washed-out', but light reflected off white clouds or diffused through light cloud or haze is usually satisfactory. White or silver reflectors can be used to lighten shadowed areas and reduce contrast.

OVERRIDING AUTOMATIC EXPOSURE

Most SLR cameras have a means of overriding the automatic exposure, increasing or decreasing it in steps of $1/2$ stop, up to 2 stops. Scattered white or yellow flowers over a mass of green foliage are often over-exposed, because the less reflective background dominates the metering process and gives correct exposure for the foliage, but not for the flowers. In these circumstances the automatic exposure can be overridden to reduce exposure by the equivalent of one stop or more. This will tend to under-expose the foliage but improve the exposure of the flowers.

On the other hand, a mass of white or yellow flowers with very little foliage will often be badly under-exposed. This can be corrected by increasing exposure by one, or sometimes two, stops.

It is in any case useful to bracket exposures, giving $1/2$ stop or 1 stop above and below the metered exposure if it is important to obtain a good photograph.

FILMS

Film speed has already been discussed, but films also vary appreciably in their colour-rendering, some being 'warm' with a bias towards red colouration, so that all pinks and mauves appear as shades of red; others are 'cold', with an overall bluish bias. Neither extreme is satisfactory for plant photography. Most photographs in this book were taken with Agfachrome 100 ISO.

Some blue flowers are difficult to reproduce on film, tending to appear mauve or even pink. This is due to to the presence of red pigments in the flower as well as the obvious blue. Improved results can be obtained by photographing them in the shade, and slightly underexposed. A pale blue filter may also help.

Whether to use print film or film for transparencies depends on the purpose for which the pictures are intended. Transparencies are usually preferred for publication in books, magazines and calendars, and are essential for projection for lectures etc. For normal domestic and holiday records, prints are generally more convenient. Cibachrome prints from transparencies are relatively resistant to fading when exposed to light, although they should not be exposed to direct sunlight for extended periods.

5

ALPENGARTEN SCHYNIGE PLATTE

For the traveller wishing to become familiar with the plants of the Bernese Oberland, a good place to start is the Alpengarten Schynige Platte. Here, it is claimed, are examples of about 80% of the plants that occur above the tree-line in Switzerland. The Alpengarten is within easy reach of Interlaken (see Excursion 1, p.49) situated at an altitude of 1,950m(6,400ft)-2,000m(6,560ft), with access by rack-and-pinion railway, the Schynige Platte Bahn. The railway was opened in 1893, and the parent company, the Berner Oberland Bahn (BOB) was involved in the earliest discussions about the formation of an Alpine Garden. The first proposals were made in 1905 by a small group which included the Director of BOB and Professor E. Fischer, of the Berne Botanical Gardens. However, it was not until further proposals were made in 1925, that a scheme was put into effect, beginning with the formation of the Verein Alpengarten Schynige Platte (The Schynige Platte Alpine Garden Society) in 1927. The Society would own and administer the Alpine Garden. The first President, Hans Itten, was a lawyer of Interlaken and served for 30 years. Work on the construction of the Garden began in 1928, and it was opened on July 6th 1929. The building providing accommodation for staff and facilities for students was opened in 1931 and renovated and extended in 1983/84 to include a museum and teaching laboratory. Courses organised by Professors of the University of Berne have taken place regularly since 1932. The University also provides technical advice. Throughout its history, the Alpengarten has had a close relationship with the railway. All materials required for use in the Garden have to be transported on the railway – including all the water required for domestic purposes, but the Garden attracts many visitors every summer, most of whom travel on the train. Very few make the steep 1400m(4600ft) climb on foot from Wilderswil or Bönigen. Access to the Garden is directly from the end of the Schynige Platte station platform.

At first sight the Alpine Garden appears to be little more than a fenced-off section of the mountain side, carrying the short wiry grasses and alpine plants typical of the area. However, by careful management, and taking advantage of the differences in habitat within the Garden, the range of habitats has been expanded to enable many more plants, and associations of plants, to be represented. Indeed, of about 620 species of flowering plants and ferns found above the tree-line in Switzerland, about 500 are represented in the Garden.

The Alpine Garden is located on the flank of the Schynige Platte, just below the summit and facing mainly east and south-east, but because there is a central mound there are many small areas with exposure to north, south and west also. To the north-east the mound falls away steeply as an exposed rock face, but otherwise the rock-strewn grassy slopes merge with the adjacent slopes of the mountain outside the Garden. Winding footpaths and flights of steps provide reasonably easy access to all parts of the Garden and also form the boundaries of the various plant communities (see Fig 1). The difference in elevation between the lowest path and the highest point is about 30m(nearly 100ft), and on the main route around the Garden there are about 50 steps and some fairly steep sections of the path. It is not suitable for wheel-chairs. The total area of the Garden is only 0.83ha(2 acres).

The Schynige Platte, like much of this part of the Bernese Oberland, is formed of intensely folded Jurassic limestone and slate, and this has a major influence on the naturally-occurring flora of the Garden and on the range of plants introduced from elsewhere; but measures have been taken (see p.41) to ensure that lime-hating plants also can be established here. Incidently, the 'shining plates' or 'Schynige Platte' refers to the shining appearance of exposed surfaces of the slate when wet, such as can be seen near the railway at the top of the mountain.

The Garden is covered in snow during mid or late October, and the overhead equipment of the Schynige Platte Bahn is dismantled for the winter. Opening-up in the spring usually entails considerable excavation of snow, both on the railway and in the Garden, where paths are cleared and winter damage repaired, the Garden staff having arrived as soon as the railway is operational early in June. The Garden is usually open to visitors by the end of June but sometimes this has to be delayed until early July.

The Garden is maintained by 3 or 4 women who live in the staff hostel for the duration of the summer season; and a man, Fritz Feuz, well known to regular visitors, who has worked there for 18 years and travels up on the railway each day from his home in Unterseen. One of their important duties is to label a few representative plants of each species as they come into flower, and to remove the labels after flowering.

Fifteen plant communities are represented in the garden, and their locations are shown on the plan (Fig 1 p.34). Four of the plant communities occupy a large proportion of the Garden's area, and all are types of grassland with accompanying herbaceous plants, which are typical 'alpines' surviving the long winter period under the snow. They are at their best soon after the snow melts. Later in the season a different range of plants becomes prominent, including many that would not ordinarily be regarded as 'alpines', but as herbaceous plants of gardens. This interesting juxtaposition of different kinds of plants arises because of the location of the Alpine Garden: at about 2000m(6,560ft) it is at about the level of the tree-line for that part of Switzerland. It is therefore within the altitude range both for alpine plants living predominantly higher than Schynige Platte, and for sub-alpine or predominantly lowland plants. Most plants in the wild can be found over a considerable range of heights.

TABLE 1

RANGE OF ALTITUDE OF SOME REPRESENTATIVE ALPINE PLANTS IN THEIR NATURAL HABITATS IN EUROPE
(ALTITUDE OF ALPINE GARDEN: 1,950-2,000m)

Alpine Plants growing in Alpine Garden at Schynige Platte	Natural Range of Altitude Height above Sea Level			
	min m	max m	min ft	max ft
Eritrichium nanum	2,500	3,600	8,200	11,800
Ranunculus glacialis	2,300	4,250	7,500	13,909
Androsace helvetica	2,000	3,500	6,500	11,500
Ranunculus parnassifolius	1,900	2,900	6,234	9,515
Anemone baldensis	1,800	3,000	5,900	9,800
Ranunculus pyrenaeus	1,700	2,800	5,600	9,200
Sempervivum montanum	1,500	3,200	4,900	10,500
Geum reptans	1,500	2,800	4,900	9,200
Campanula thyrsoides	1,500	2,300	4,900	7,500
Gentiana acaulis	1,400	3,000	4,600	9,800
Ranunculus alpestris	1,300	3,000	4,265	9,800
Vaccinium vitis-idaea	0	3,050	0	10,000
Gentiana verna,	0	3,000	0	9,800
Dryas octopetala	0	2,500	0	8,200

The Garden is at the upper end of the range for many other species that occur mainly at lower levels but are nevertheless mountain plants. Many of these species have been taken successfully into cultivation, and are more familiar in gardens than in the wild. It may seem inappropriate to find delphiniums and monkshoods, meadow-rues, campanulas, cranesbills and storksbills and many others growing vigorously in 'herbaceous borders' in the Alpine Garden. However, they appear as very different plants when growing in their natural habitats, near their limits of altitude, many of them as hay-meadow plants, dwarfed by competition.

TABLE 2

MAXIMUM ALTITUDE OF TYPICAL HERBACEOUS PLANTS IN THEIR NATURAL HABITATS IN EUROPE

Herbaceous Plants growing in Alpine Garden at Schynige Platte	Maximum Altitude in Natural Habitats Height above Sea Level	
	m	ft
Gypsophila repens	2,900	9,500
Epilobium angustifolium	2,500	8,200
Aconitum napellus	2,500	8,200
Thalictrum aquilegifolium	2,500	8,200
Campanula rotundifolia	2,200	7,900
Delphinium elatum	2,000	6,500
Astrantia major	2,000	6,500
Campanula glomerata	1,700	5,600

Fig 1 The Plant Communities of the Alpine Garden

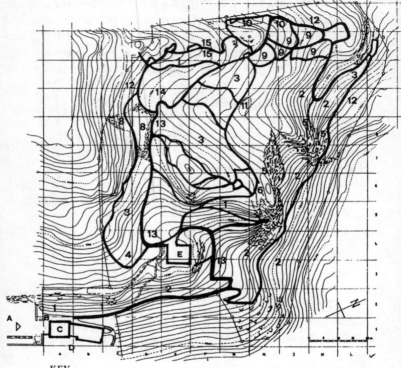

KEY

1. Blue-grass meadow
2. Rusty-sedge (red-brown sedge) meadow
3. Alpine pasture
4. Mat-grass meadow
5. Dwarf shrubby heath plants
6. Plants of wind-blown ridges
7. Plants of calcareous rocks
8. Plants of calcareous screes
9. Plants of non-calcareous habitats
   (acid or neutral rocks, screes, etc)
10. Snow-hollow plants
11. Alpine bog plants
12. Green alder scrub
13. Tall herbaceous plants
14. High-nitrogen plants
15. Medicinal plants

A. Railway Station
B. Entrance and exit
C. Laboratory, student
   and staff hostel, and
   exhibition room
D. Propagation & seed bed
E. Viewpoint with seats

A Closer Look at the Alpine Garden

The admission kiosk at the end of the railway platform is part of the building that houses a laboratory for teaching and research, and living accommodation for the Garden Staff. It also contains an exhibition room, open to the public, giving information about the flora, fauna and geology of the Garden and particularly about the management of the alpine meadows and pastures. Research on this subject has been carried out, within and beyond the Garden, by Dr Lüdi of the University of Berne.

A detailed vegetation map of the Garden, in colour, is also displayed in the exhibition room, usefully expanding the information in the sketch-plan in the guide book.

The Grassland Communities

At the entrance to the Garden, and along the first section of the footpath, the steep slope has been excavated to accommodate the path, leaving a rock wall which provides a suitable habitat for a number of plants which have been placed there for easy viewing at a convenient height. These include *Leontopodium alpinum* (edelweiss) [cover], which every tourist hopes to see, but which flowers later than most of the plants typifying the 'Alpine Spring'.

The slope above and below the path is an example of the 'blue-grass meadow' plant community ('1' on Fig 1), dominated by the grass *Sesleria caerulea*, which typically occurs on steep south-facing slopes over calcareous rocks. The soil here is stony and quick-drying. Other kinds of grassland are represented in the Garden, some of limited extent, the variations depending on aspect, slope, and drainage, and on the amount of soil that has accumulated. The 'Rusty Sedge Meadow' is distinguished by the presence of a sedge *Carex fuliginosa* (syn. *C.ferruginea* (red-brown sedge), with other sedges and grasses ('2' on Fig 1). It occurs over limestones under moister conditions than those favouring blue-grass meadow. Over impoverished soils *Nardus stricta* (mat grass) becomes dominant, growing in dense tufts interspersed with colourful herbs ('4' on Fig 1). The meadows of blue-grass, red-brown sedge and mat grass tend to merge in the Alpine Garden, but the main interest, common to all three is the range of attractive herbaceous plants associated with them.

The early visitor, arriving as the last of the snow is melting, will find wet banks with the remains of dead vegetation from the previous year, but already enlivened by *Crocus albiflorus* (white crocus) [Pl.5], delicately fringed mauve flowers of *Soldanella alpina* (alpine snowbell) [Pl.5] and the small mauve 'pom-poms' of *Globularia nudicaulis* (leafless-stemmed globularia). These are soon followed by clumps of *Primula elatior* (oxlip), *Pulsatilla alpina* (alpine pasque flower) [Pl.6], and *Anemone narcissiflora* (narcissus-flowered anemone) [Pl.15]. *Primula auricula* (auricula) [Pl.3] appears in rocky crevices, or on grassy slopes with the intensely-blue *Gentiana clusii* and *Gentiana acaulis* (trumpet gentians) [Pl.10], dark-red *Pedicularis recutita* (beakless red lousewort) and red *Trifolium alpinum* (alpine clover) [Pl.9]. Other louseworts in grassy areas include pale yellow *Pedicularis foliosa* (leafy lousewort) [Pl.8] and *Pedicularis verticillata* (verticillate lousewort) [Pl.8] which is pinkish red.

A little later the striking pale yellow spikes of *Campanula thyrsoides* (yellow bellflower) [Pl.8] emerge, and also the elegant white flowers of *Paradisia liliastrum*

(St. Bruno's lily) [Pl.13]. Orchids in the Garden include *Coeloglossum viride* (frog orchid), *Gymnadenia conopsea* (fragrant orchid) [Pl.7], *Nigritella nigra* (black vanilla orchid) and *Traunsteinera globosa* (round-headed orchid). Most of the meadow plants in the Garden are dispersed in a 'natural' way, but some that are not native to this part of Switzerland are planted in obvious groups, like the magnificent clumps of *Gentiana angustifolia* planted near the Garden entrance and by the path up to the mound from near the limestone scree bed.

Where short wiry grass in a sparse soil cover gives way to exposed rock surfaces, *Gentiana verna* (the blue spring gentian) [Pl.10] and *Dryas octopetala* (mountain avens) [Pl.11] flourish, with *Globularia cordifolia* (matted globularia) [Pl.11], *Potentilla aurea* (golden cinquefoil) and *Potentilla crantzii* (alpine cinquefoil). *Viola calcarata* (long-spurred pansy) also occurs on dry grassy slopes, and *Antennaria dioica* (catsfoot) under more acid conditions. The yellow form of the alpine pasque flower, *Pulsatilla alpina apiifolia* [Pl.6] also favours more acid conditions than the white form. Such conditions can arise even over limestone, where debris of vegetation accumulates with only partial breakdown where low temperatures prevail. These are the grasslands that predominate in the alpine zone. Where there are deeper and richer soils the more prolific flora of the cattle pastures and hay meadows occurs. These achieve the most spectacular development in the sub-alpine zone, in cleared areas of the forested zone and on the valley floors at 1,000-1,600m(3,281-5,250ft) [Pl.13]. Their places in the Garden are marked '3' on Fig 1. Regular cutting or grazing of alpine meadows is necessary to maintain their character. Uncut grass and sedges can become frozen into a layer of snow and pulled away if an avalanche occurs, leaving exposed rock and starting a process of erosion that cannot readily be reversed. Examples of this effect are apparent on the SE-facing slopes to the north of the Alpine Garden, towards the Oberberghorn.

HIGH-NITROGEN PLANTS

Another prominent type of plant community is that associated with cattle sheds and other places where cattle congregate for shade or shelter. In such areas, where large amounts of nitrogenous manures accumulate and are washed into the soil, there develops a coarse and impoverished flora of relatively few rampant species against which the majority of mountain plants cannot compete. This flora is reproduced in the Alpine Garden by heavy manuring of one area ('14' on Fig 1) and includes *Ranunculus aconitifolius* (white crowfoot), *Chenopodium bonus-henricus* (good King Henry), *Rumex* spp. (docks and sorrels), and *Alchemilla vulgaris* (common lady's mantle). *Urtica dioica* (stinging nettle) can also occur in disturbed ground in these areas, up to 3,150m(10,300ft)

TALL HERBACEOUS PLANTS

In areas of the Garden where soil has accumulated and snow lies deeply in the winter, various tall herbaceous plants flourish ('13' on Fig 1). Indeed, the steep path leading up to the main viewpoint ('E' on Fig 1) is flanked by such plants, giving almost the effect of an herbaceous border. These plants die down at the onset of winter, surviving with the protection of a deep layer of snow.

There is little evidence of their presence when the snow melts, except for bedraggled remains lying on the surface, but growth soon begins and proceeds rapidly. However, their need to develop substantial stems and leaves before flowering means that they do not reach their peak until late August or early September, although the time at which the maximum number of plant species are flowering throughout the Garden is in early August. Because the tall herbaceous plants need a considerable time to complete their development they do not feature at altitudes much higher than Schynige Platte; above this height the period free from snow is too short and the environment too harsh.

The development of the tall herbaceous plants when 'gardened' on Schynige Platte is much more vigorous than when they are in competition in the wild, eg. in hay meadows. A number of the genera include plants that are familiar in gardens eg *Delphinium, Aconitum, Thalictrum* [Pl.14], *Eryngium, Astrantia* [Pl.14], *Senecio* and *Geranium*.

SCREE PLANTS

Screes formed of rock fragments, weathered from exposed rock faces, are predominantly a feature of the alpine zone, and the plants associated with them are relatively unfamiliar to lowland gardeners, and therefore of particular interest.

The calcareous scree in the Garden is of fragmented limestone, similar to other screes in the surrounding area ('8' on Fig 1). The plants represented include several of the white-flowered mountain buttercups, including *Ranunculus glacialis* (glacier crowfoot) [Pl.4] which has been found at the highest point of the Bernese Oberland, on the Finsteraarhorn, at 4,250m(13,900ft). It can also be found down to 2,300m(7,500ft) in the wild, but is gardened successfully at the Schynige Platte, together with *Ranunculus alpestris* (alpine buttercup) and *Ranunculus parnassifolius* (Parnassus-leaved buttercup) [Pl.3] with its shiny heart-shaped leaves resembling those of *Parnassia palustris* (grass of Parnassus). The pink-flowered and sweetly scented *Thlaspi rotundifolia* (round-leaved pennycress) [Pl.3] emerges from between the rocks, and rosettes of *Geum reptans* (creeping avens) [Pl.3] with yellow flowers, extend long red runners, like strawberry runners, forming new rosettes whenever conditions are favourable. Scattered groups of *Papaver burseri* and *Papaver kerneri* (alpine poppies) produce delicate-looking white and yellow flowers. Several dwarf shrubs lie prostrate amongst the scree fragments or spread out over rocks and boulders sending long roots into crevices and deep into the scree. These include *Polygala chamaebuxus* (shrubby milkwort) [Pl.16] with flowers reminiscent of long-eared bats, mostly with pale-yellow 'ears' and orange 'snouts'. The dwarf willows, including *Salix reticulata* (net-leaved willow) [Pl.16], *Salix retusa* (blunt-leaved willow) and *Salix serpyllifolia* (thyme-leaved willow) all have small erect catkins, standing above the prostrate leafy shoots. The low wall of limestone blocks limiting the scree beside the footpath accommodates various small plants in sheltered nooks and crannies, eg *Viola biflora* (yellow wood violet) [Pl.4] with small bright-yellow flowers, neatly lined on the lip, and *Veronica aphylla* (leafless-stemmed veronica) [Pl.4] having small rosettes of leaves with leafless upright stems, each carrying 2 or 3 typical blue *Veronica* flowers. *Veronica fruticans* (rock speedwell) [Pl.12] is a small shrubby plant, the stem woody at the base, and the blue flowers unusual in having a narrow red ring around the centre, at the base of the petals.

To enable plants of acidic or neutral soils and rocks to be grown and displayed at the Alpine Garden, large amounts of rock and gravel were brought in from the Grimsel area and used to construct a series of acid beds ('9' on Fig 1). The materials were brought up on the Schynige Platte Bahn and numerous local volunteers, including school children, helped to move it all from the station into the Garden, an event apparently still fresh in the minds of some of those volunteers 60 years later! Considerable problems were experienced because water drained from the limestone beds and damaged the calcifuge plants but modification of the drainage system appears to have made it possible to exclude lime from the acid beds satisfactorily. Plants growing successfully in the acid beds include *Androsace carnea* (pink rock-jasmine), *Gentiana punctata* (spotted gentian) [Pl.10], *Rhodiola rosea* (roseroot), *Oxyria digyna* (mountain sorrel) [P.11], *Vitaliana primuliflora* (vitaliana) and the shrubby *Salix helvetica* (Swiss willow). *Potentilla aurea* (golden cinquefoil), *Linaria alpina* (alpine toadflax) [Pl.11], *Primula hirsuta* (hairy primrose) and *Sempervivum wulfenii* (Wulfen's houseleek) are well established but the much prized *Eritrichium nanum* (King of the Alps) has so far proved much more difficult.

TREES AND SHRUBS

Because the Garden is at about the height of the tree-line in this part of Switzerland the few trees present, mainly the coniferous *Picea abies* (Norway spruce) are slow-growing and stunted, mostly in situations with a southerly aspect and backed by rocks that give some shelter and reflected heat from the sun. *Sorbus aucuparia* (mountain ash or rowan) is also present adjacent to the main viewing platform 'E' on Fig 1. Above the tree-line the shrubs are mostly short and dense but *Alnus viridis* (green alder) ('12' on Fig 1) has characteristics that enable it to withstand avalanches without suffering major damage. It is very flexible and although flattened by avalanches, which simply slide over the bushes, they soon right themselves and continue growth. Their effect is to protect the surface layers of soil from erosion. In addition, they carry root-nodules containing a nitrogen-fixing fungus by means of which the nitrogen content of the soil can be increased. *Alnus viridis* is therefore a useful pioneering shrub which can help to build up plant populations and stabilize screes. Plants associated with it tend to be from the 'tall herbaceous' group such as *Aquilegia alpina* (alpine columbine), but in the Garden it is accompanied by *Cortusa matthiola* (alpine bells).

Dwarf and shrubby heath plants ('5' on Fig 1) occur where a thick layer of raw humus has developed over flat limestone ledges and terraces. Such conditions allow lime-hating plants to grow despite the underlying calcareous rocks. Plants of this kind growing in the Alpine Garden include *Vaccinium vitis-idaea* (cowberry), *Vaccinium myrtillus* (bilberry) [Pl.16], *Rhododendron ferrugineum* (alpenrose) [Pl.16] and *Rhododendron hirsutum* (hairy alpenrose), the latter species being relatively lime-tolerant. *Juniperus communis* (common juniper) also forms low spreading bushes. In a fairly sheltered place, just before the point at which the path from the entrance turns left and starts rising steeply, there is a bush of *Sorbus chamaemespilus* (false medlar) with attractive pink flowers in early summer. Another bush, near the the lower end of the acid beds ('9' on Fig 1) is *Lonicera caerulea* (blue-fruited honeysuckle) with small yellow bell-like flowers, also in a position that is not too much exposed to severe winds, in contrast to the plants of a wind-blown ridge ('6' on Fig 1). At this point on the top of the central mound, strong winds can blow from any point of the compass, and any snow that falls is rapidly blown away. Plants in such situations have to withstand extreme low temperatures and desiccation, for although a plant's roots may descend deep into rock crevices the water there may be frozen and unavailable. One of the plants that can withstand such unfavourable conditions is *Loiseleuria procumbens* (creeping azalea) [Pl.16], but just below the ridge some other shrubby heath plants ('5' on Fig 1) are established.

OTHER PLANT ASSOCIATIONS

Relatively small numbers of plants are associated in the Garden with vertical rock faces, and with an artificially constructed alpine bog and snow hollows over limestone and acidic rocks.

Crevices in calcareous outcrops and rock faces ('7' on Fig 1) and amongst boulders are colonised by various deep-rooted plants such as *Primula auricula* (auricula) [Pl.3] and *Hedysarum hedysaroides* (alpine sanfoin). *Saxifraga cuneifolia* (spoon-leaved saxifrage) and *Erinus alpinus* (fairy foxglove) also favour rocky places. A recently installed block of tufa (a sponge-like calcareous rock) provides a suitable habitat for some of the high-alpine cushion-plants including *Androsace helvetica* (Swiss rock-jasmine) [Pl.11] at a convenient height for viewing the neat flower-covered hummocks.

The alpine bog ('11' on Fig 1) has proved difficult to maintain sufficiently wet during summer. Apart from various sedges there are a few flowering plants, eg *Caltha palustris* (marsh marigold), *Menyanthes trifoliata* (bogbean) and *Potentilla palustris* (marsh cinquefoil)

Where depressions in the ground are filled with deep accumulations of snow, or where avalanche material accumulates regularly, snow persists long into summer, leaving only a very short period free from snow when it eventually melts. Such places are known as snow-hollows or snow coombs. No natural snow-hollows exist in the Garden, but artificial ones have been created ('10' on Fig 1). Plants established there include *Saxifraga stellaris* (starry saxifrage), *Primula minima* (least primrose) and *Salix herbacea* (least willow).

There is also in the Garden a section for medicinal plants ('15' on Fig 1) which are grown in beds terraced with railway sleepers. Most of the plants are fairly late-flowering and are not seen to advantage during the 'alpine spring'. They include specimens of *Veratrum album* (white false helleborine) and *Gentiana lutea* (great yellow gentian), which are very similar before flowering but the very poisonous *Veratrum album* has alternate leaves, which are pleated and downy on the underside, whilst *Gentiana lutea* has opposite leaves which are ribbed, and smooth on the underside.

The Alpengarten Schynige Platte is a valuable source of botanical information, in a magnificent setting. Remember, however, that despite all the rules and recommendations concerning the naming of plants, there are differences of opinion from one country to another, and one should not be too disturbed to find inconsistencies between British and Swiss floras in the naming of a few plants.

6

EASY EXCURSIONS
from
INTERLAKEN

INTERLAKEN	567m Δ (1,890ft)

This chapter describes easy ways to travel on public transport from Interlaken to areas where you are likely to see a range of plants in flower in late June and early July. The notes for each excursion give full details of travel arrangements, that were operational in 1992, and a short account of the locality.

The authors have always visited the mountains during the early spring but have not always found the same flowers at their best in the same place at the same time in different years. So there can be no guarantee that you will find all the plants we discuss on your first visit! Many factors affect flowering; weather conditions, grazing, mowing, erosion, as well as natural fluctuations in plant populations. A wide range of plants such as gentians, pasque flowers, violas, campanulas, potentillas and ranunculus and many orchids are widespread throughout the region. We have not attempted to make a comprehensive list for each site, but only mention the plants that we found most photogenic on each excursion!

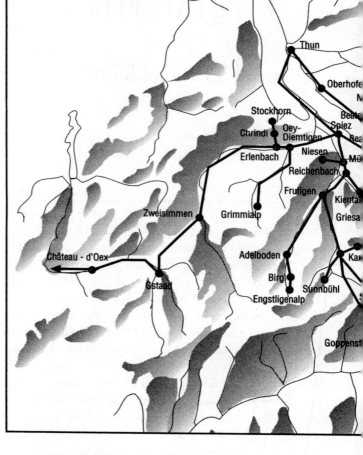

Fig 2 Easy Excursions in the Bernese Oberland

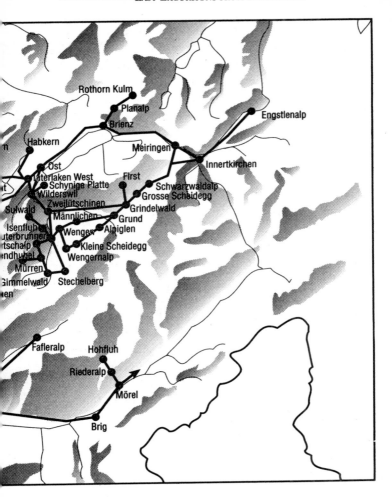

We shall draw your attention to footpaths which will enable those who can walk comfortably at these altitudes to explore further, to enjoy more of the scenery and find a wider range of interesting plants.

There is a restaurant or hotel near the destination of nearly all the excursions, even in very remote areas, but it is always a good idea to have a bottle of water and a light snack in your ruck-sack even if you intend to sample the local fare.

The times given for the walks are generous to allow plenty of time for enjoying the scenery and looking at the plants. The times given on the sign-posts are for steady walking by someone who is very fit

Do remember to be prepared for the very rapid changes in weather that occur frequently in the mountains. Several layers of clothing are preferable; stout walking-shoes or boots, waterproofs, sunglasses and some form of head-covering for protection from strong sun are essential. Sun protection cream is also essential for most people, and an insect repellent cream is often very useful.

If you want to be able to identify the plants you see, take with you a notebook, a camera, plenty of films, and a copy of: *Alpine Flowers of Britain and Europe* by C. Grey-Wilson & Marjorie Blamey

REMEMBER You may only take notes and photographs home.

EXCURSION VIA WILDERSWIL   584m Δ (1,926ft)

TRAIN:	Interlaken Ost to Wilderswil	5min
BUS:	Interlaken West to Wilderswil	9min

Wilderswil is a quiet village with many Guest Houses and Hotels and picturesque chalets forming a distinct rural community on the banks of the fast running Lütschine river. An interesting Village Museum is being developed in the old mill buildings to illustrate the history and the rural crafts of the area, with a small nature garden and pool on the edge of the mill stream. The mountain railway running up the Schynige Platte starts from Wilderswil Station.

E X C U R S I O N   1

SCHYNIGE PLATTE   1,950m Δ (6,400ft)-2,000m Δ (6,560ft)

TRAIN:	Wilderswil to Schynige Platte	52min

The mountain railway, Schynige Platte Bahn, winds slowly up the mountain, first through the village, then on through beech woods, then through conifer forest, before reaching the alpine pastures above the tree-line. There are magnificent views over Interlaken, Brienzersee and Thunersee and nearing the end of the journey you are surrounded by snow-covered peaks. As you approach Schynige Platte station you see plates of mica in the rock face; these shining plates which are especially prominent in wet weather are responsible for the mountain's name. The entrance to the Alpengarten is at the end of the station platform. A full account of the garden is given in

Chapter 5. There are many footpaths from Schynige Platte. Those going down the mountain are very steep and are not recommended for inexperienced walkers. There are a number of paths through the alpine meadows that surround the Alpengarten and with the aid of a map you can plan relatively easy walks in magnificent scenery and see wide expanses of the natural flora of this part of the Oberland.

EXCURSIONS VIA GRINDELWALD   1,050m Δ (3,445ft)

TRAIN: Interlaken Ost to Grindelwald   45min

The train calls at Wilderswil and then follows the river Lütschine to Zweilütschinen where the train divides into two sections (make sure you are in a coach labelled 'Grindelwald'). The eastern branch follows the Schwarze Lütschine up the steep wooded valley to Grindelwald. Grindelwald has many modern hotels, shops and leisure facilities set in flower-filled alpine meadows in the shadow of the north face of the Eiger. Tourists started coming to the village towards the end of the 17th century and it has been becoming increasingly popular ever since! In good weather the resort can be very crowded, but once you start on one of the excursions you will soon reach more peaceful surroundings in spectacular scenery.

EXCURSION 2

GRINDELWALD FIRST   2,200 △ (7,218ft)

TRAIN:	Interlaken Ost to Grindelwald	45min
WALK:	to First Gondelbahn	10min
GONDELBAHN:	to First	20min

Walk about half a mile up the hill from Grindelwald railway station to the Gondelbahn which is on the left-hand side of the main street. The journey to the top station of the gondelbahn provides wonderful views of the mountains and alpine meadows and pastures but there are two intermediate stations where you may get out to explore at ground-level using well-marked but very steep paths. There is a wide range of plants growing within a few hundred yards of the top of the Gondelbahn in the pastures surrounding the restaurant. We have found a large number of species on the short walk towards the lower station of the First-Oberjoch skilift which stands on the edge of a deep steep-sided gully. At the edges of patches of melting snow in the lower part of this gully we have photographed carpets of *Soldanella alpina* (alpine snowbell) [Pl.5] and *Soldanella pusilla* (dwarf snowbell) [Pl.5]. *Thlaspi rotundifolium* (round-leaved penny cress) [Pl.3] and *Hutchinsia alpina* (chamois cress) [Pl.12] can be found in the gravel banks along the edges of the stream running through the same gully. On the grassy bank above the track leading down to Grindel there are large patches of *Gentiana acaulis* (trumpet gentian) [Pl.10] and *Gentiana verna* (spring gentian) [Pl.10], with small clumps of *Primula farinosa* (birdseye primrose) [Pl.9]. Many people take the undulating Wanderweg westwards along the top of the ridge to Bachalpsee, a mountain lake, altitude 2265m(7431ft)), others walk downhill and rejoin the gondelbahn at Grindel. If you make your return trip on the gondelbahn from First, you will have another opportunity to enjoy the mountain scenery and the meadow flowers as you travel quietly back to Grindelwald.

E X C U R S I O N 3

SCHWARZWALDALP		1,454m △ (4,770ft)
TRAIN:	Interlaken Ost to Grindelwald	45min
POST-BUS:	Grindelwald to Schwarzwaldalp	50min
WALK :	Schwarzwaldalp to Rosenlaui	1hr
POST-BUS:	Rosenlaui to Meiringen	35min
TRAIN:	Meiringen to Brienz	12min
TRAIN:	Brienz to Interlaken Ost	25min
or BOAT:	Brienz to Interlaken Ost	1hr 5min

This excursion makes full use of public transport to take you over the Grosse Scheidegg pass, altitude 1,961m(6,434ft), from Grindelwald (see p.50), amid rugged mountain scenery to Schwarzwaldalp where you can leave the post-bus for a gentle walk through the woods and fields of the lower part of Scheidegg Alp.

In the damp wooded areas running beside the road there are large colonies of *Dactylorhiza fuchsii* (common spotted orchid) and *Dactylorhiza majalis* (broad-leaved marsh orchid) [Pl.7]. There are occasional plants of *Moneses uniflora* (one-flowered wintergreen). *Pedicularis verticillata* (verticillate lousewort) [Pl.8] occurs frequently. On this walk, several years ago, we found a strangely isolated clump of *Cypripedium calceolus* (lady's slipper orchid) [Pl.15], growing well away from any of the few known sites that remain in relatively inaccessible valleys.

On this excursion you may wish to make one or more diversions to three non-botanical tourist attractions:

The glacier gorge at Rosenlaui;

The Reichenbach Falls, made famous in one of Conan Doyle's Sherlock Holmes stories, a 20min walk from the post-bus stop at Zwirgi;

The Aare Gorge, 1 mile from Meiringen;

before taking the train from Meiringen to Brienz, where you have the choice of returning to Interlaken by either train or boat.

E X C U R S I O N   4

WENGERNALP	2,061m Δ (6,762ft)-1,873m Δ (6,145ft)

TRAIN:	Interlaken Ost to Grindelwald	45min
TRAIN:	Grindelwald to Kleine Scheidegg	36min
WALK:	Kleine Scheidegg to Wengernalp	1hr
TRAIN:	Wengernalp to Lauterbrunnen	45min
TRAIN:	Lauterbrunnen to Interlaken Ost	23min

At Grindelwald (see p.50) station, change on to the mountain railway going to Kleine Scheidegg which is a tourist and ski-centre with hotels and restaurants and a station with three separate train services, one for the Jungfraujoch, another for Lauterbrunnen and the third for Grindelwald. The station platforms are always busy, but there are peaceful footpaths among beautiful scenery, providing easy ways to see a wide range of plants. The path to Wengernalp station crosses gently sloping pastures filled with interesting plants. As the snow melts, sheets of *Crocus albiflorus* (white crocus) [Pl.5] with just a few plants of *Crocus vernus* (purple crocus) [Pl.5] among them, cover large areas of pastures. *Soldanella alpina* (alpine snowbell) [Pl.5], *Gagea fistulosa* (yellow gagea) [Pl.15] and *Caltha palustris* (marsh marigold) share damp hollows with the insectivorous *Pinguicula alpina* (alpine butterwort) [Pl.15]. Dry grassy banks are filled with mixtures of *Pulsatilla alpina* (alpine pasque flower) [Pl.6], *Phyteuma spicatum* (spiked rampion) [Pl.13], *Trifolium alpinum* (alpine clover) [Pl.9], *Ligusticum mutellina* (alpine lovage) [Pl.13] and the occasional *Campanula barbata* (bearded campanula) [Pl.13]. The damper pastures contain many orchids such as *Gymnadenia albida* (small white orchid) [Pl.7], *Gymnadenia conopsea* (fragrant orchid) [Pl.7], *Dactylorhiza fuchsii* (common spotted orchid), *Dactylorhiza majalis* (broad-leaved marsh orchid) [Pl.7] and *Orchis mascula* (early purple orchid) with *Trollius europaeus* (globeflower) [Pl.15] as well as myriads of *Gentiana acaulis* (trumpet gentian) [Pl.10], *Gentiana clusii* (Clusius's gentian) and the rather less frequent *Gentiana bavarica* (Bavarian gentian). *Rhododendron ferruginea* (alpenrose) [Pl.16] and *Vaccinium myrtillus* (bilberry) [Pl.16] shelter clumps of *Pulsatilla alpina apiifolia* (yellow alpine pasque flower) [Pl.6]. Passengers on the trains from Wengernalp, passing through Wengen, on their way to Lauterbrunnen, have spectacular views of the deep glaciated valley and waterfalls before changing trains to return to Interlaken Ost.

E X C U R S I O N 5
MÄNNLICHEN TO KLEINE SCHEIDEGG

2,230m Δ (7,317ft)-2,061m Δ (6,762ft)

TRAIN:	Interlaken Ost to Grindelwald	45min
TRAIN:	Grindelwald to Grund	10min

GONDELBAHN:	Grund to Männlichen	30min
WALK:	Männlichen to Kleine Scheidegg	2hrs
TRAIN:	Kleine Scheidegg to Lauterbrunnen	1hr
TRAIN:	Lauterbrunnen to Interlaken Ost	25mins

At Grindelwald (see p.50) station change on to the mountain railway going to Kleine Scheidegg and travel to Grund which is the first stopping place. As you leave Grund Station turn right and walk the short distance to the gondelbahn which is at the far end of a large car-park. Remain in your gondola as you pass through the middle station, and if you look carefully at the ground as you continue up the mountain, you may see marmots playing near their burrows. The plants to be found around the top station and the views over Lauterbrunnen and the Lütschental make the journey worth while, but if the weather is good, and most of the snow has melted, you should find a great variety of plants in flower beside the Bergweg to Kleine Scheidegg. The path [Pl.1] is well marked with a good surface and has a gentle downward slope for most of the way, but there is no shelter if you are caught in a storm. The 'official walking time' is 1hr 15mins, but it usually takes us 2-3hrs to make the journey and photograph the plants!

Among the short grasses of the pasture around the upper station and the restaurant we have found *Alchemilla alpina* (alpine lady's mantle) [Pl.9], *Androsace chamaejasme* (ciliate rock-jasmine), *Antennaria dioica* (catsfoot) *Carlina acaulis* (stemless carline thistle), *Gentiana acaulis* (trumpet gentian) [Pl.10], *Gentiana clusii* (Clusius's gentian), *Gentiana verna* (spring gentian) [Pl.10], *Gymnadenia albida* (small white orchid) [Pl.7], *Homogyne alpina* (alpine coltsfoot) [Pl.8], *Lloydia serotina*

(Snowdon Lily) [Pl.9], *Primula farinosa* (birdseye primrose) [Pl.9], *Pulsatilla vernalis* (spring pasque flower) [Pl.6] and *Trifolium alpinum* (alpine clover) [Pl.9].

Large patches of *Rhododendron ferrugineum* (alpenrose) [Pl.16] cover the steep slopes below the path and damp hollows are filled with *Trollius europaeus* (globeflower) [Pl.15], *Soldanella alpina* (alpine snowbell) [Pl.5] and *Oxyria digyna* (mountain sorrel) [Pl.11]. *Ranunculus alpestris* (alpine buttercup) and *Ranunculus montanus* are found on the edges of drifts of snow still lying in the deeper gulleys. *Dryas octopetala* (mountain avens) [Pl.11], *Gentiana brachyphylla* (short-leaved gentian) [Pl.10], *Potentilla crantzii* (alpine cinquefoil), *Primula hirsuta* (hairy primrose) and *Saxifraga burseriana* (one-flowered cushion saxifrage) and *Vaccinium myrtillus* (bilberry) [Pl.16] are found growing in rock crevices and among stones and boulders, whilst *Loiseleuria procumbens* (creeping azalea) [Pl.16] colonises windswept rocks, and *Viola biflora* (yellow wood violet) [Pl.4] grows in damp conditions in the shade of large rocks and boulders. The second half of the walk crosses the Inberg valley lying between the Tschuggen and the Lauberhorn, the soil here is more acid and *Pulsatilla alpina subsp. apiifolia* (yellow alpine pasque flower) [Pl.6] is one of the prominent plants on the steep slopes on either side of the stream.

If the weather is unsuitable, or some of the party feel that they should not attempt the walk to Kleine Scheidegg, it is possible to go rapidly down to Wengen, using the cable-car which runs from the station a few hundred yards south-west of the Männlichen restaurant. A 10-minute walk through this modern alpine resort takes you to the railway station for trains to either Kleine Scheidegg or Lauterbrunnen.

EXCURSIONS VIA LAUTERBRUNNEN   796m Δ (2,612ft)

TRAIN: Interlaken Ost to Lauterbrunnen   23min

The train from Interlaken follows the Lütschine valley to Zweilütschinen, where it divides into two sections, one part taking the Schwarze Lütschine valley to Grindelwald, and the other following the Weisse Lütschine into the glaciated U-shaped Lauterbrunnen valley. The village and the valley are named after the springs (lautere Brunnen) that were the focal point of the original settlement which was sited futher up the valley than the present holiday and travel centre. The valley is enclosed by high rock walls with spectacular waterfalls cascading down from the surrounding mountains. The village has several hotels, guest houses, shops and a busy railway interchange for Wengen, Kleine Scheidegg and Mürren. As there is no car access to either Wengen or Mürren all motorists have to leave their cars in the large car-park adjoining Lauterbrunnen station and proceed by train or on foot to these villages which are perched on high ledges either side of the valley. The post-bus service to Stechelberg passes near to the entrance to the Trümmelbach falls which are enclosed in a series of caves and gorges within the Schwarz Mönch mountain. In the wide valley floor above the village there are extensive hay meadows, full of colourful flowers in June and early July. Lauterbrunnen is the starting point for excursions to the summit of the Schilthorn.

E X C U R S I O N 6

KLEINE SCHEIDEGG AND ALPIGLEN

2,061m Δ (6,752ft)-1,068m Δ (3,504ft)

TRAIN:	Interlaken Ost to Lauterbrunnen	25min
TRAIN:	Lauterbrunnen to Kleine Scheidegg	45min
WALK:	Kleine Scheidegg to Alpiglen	2hrs
TRAIN:	Alpiglen to Grindelwald	35min
TRAIN:	Grindelwald to Interlaken Ost	40min

The trains for Kleine Scheidegg leave Lauterbrunnen station from a platform adjacent to the arrival platform for trains from Interlaken, and take a much shorter route between Lauterbrunnen and Wengen on their upward journey (45min) than on the corresponding downward journey (1hr). There are good views of the mountains and the Lauterbrunnen valley, and plenty of opportunities to enjoy the flowers as you are carried up into the mountains at the gentle speed of the rack and pinion railway.

At Kleine Scheidegg walk to the Grindelwald end of the platform and then take the Bergweg which takes a fairly gentle downhill route in a north-easterly direction following the line of the railway to Alpiglen beneath the north face of the Eiger. The path is on the northern side of the railway for most of its length and only crosses to the southern side 500m south-west of Alpiglen station.

Although you may see pasture plants such as *Androsace chamaejasme* (ciliate rock-jasmine), *Antennaria dioica* (catsfoot), *Bartsia alpina* (alpine bartsia), *Gentiana verna* (spring gentian) [Pl.10], *Geum montanum* (alpine avens), *Gymnadenia albida* (small white orchid) [Pl.7], *Plantago alpina* (alpine plantain), *Polygonum bistorta* (bistort), *Primula farinosa* (birdseye primrose) [Pl.9] *Pulsatilla vernalis* [Pl.6], *Silene acaulis* (moss campion) [Pl.12] and *Viola lutea* (mountain pansy) near Kleine Scheidegg, most of this path crosses rough hummocky ground with many rocks and boulders which are interspersed with occasional damp hollows. There are large areas of low-growing shrubs such as *Rhododendron ferrugineum* (alpenrose) [Pl.16], *Salix reticulata* (netted willow, [Pl.16] and *Vaccinium myrtillus* (bilberry) [Pl.16] with small groups of herbaceous plants such as *Astrantia major* (great masterwort) [Pl.14] *Doronicum columnae* (heart-leaved leopardsbane), *Melampyrum nemorosum* (wood cow-wheat) and *Pulsatilla alpina subsp. apiifolia* (yellow alpine pasque flower) [Pl.6] growing on the small patches of level ground between boulders. *Caltha palustris* (marsh marigold), *Crocus albiflorus* (white crocus), [Pl.5], *Gagea fistulosa* (yellow gagea) [Pl.15], *Homogyne alpina* (alpine coltsfoot), *Linaria alpina* (alpine toadflax) [Pl.11], *Ranunculus aconitifolius* (aconite-leaved buttercup) and *Viola biflora* (yellow wood violet) [Pl.4] grow in the hollows and marshy ground on the edge of streams. The upper limit of the sparse stand of rather stunted conifers above Alpiglen Station marks the position of the tree-line; below this level the pastures contain *Biscutella laevigata* (Buckler's Mustard), *Cardamine amara* (large bittercress), and *Cardamine pratensis* (lady's smock).

The railway staff at Alpiglen station will arrange for one of the trains from Kleine Scheidegg to stop and take you down to Grindelwald where you can catch a train back to Interlaken Ost.

E X C U R S I O N   7

WENGERNALP TO WIXI AND BIGLENALP

1,873m Δ (6,245ft)-1,829m Δ (6,001ft)-1,735m Δ (5,693ft)

TRAIN:	Interlaken Ost to Lauterbrunnen	25min
TRAIN:	Lauterbrunnen to Wengernalp	35min
WALK:	Wengernalp to Wixi and return	1hr
	(Wengernalp to Biglenalp	
	& return)	2-3hr
TRAIN:	Wengernalp to Kleine Scheidegg	10min
TRAIN:	Kleine Scheidegg to Grindelwald	55min
TRAIN:	Grindelwald to Interlaken Ost	40min

This excursion takes you on the circular railway tour of the Jungfrau region with a short easy detour on foot to see alpine plants growing on rocky outcrops. At Lauterbrunnen (see p.57) station change on to the mountain railway taking the train heading for Kleine Scheidegg, leaving the train at Wengernalp, which is the stop after Wengen. As you leave the station continue uphill and take the path through the tunnel under the railway line, just above the station. Three footpaths meet on the south side of the tunnel, take the centre one, a Berweg signed to Wixi and Biglenalp. The first part of this path, to the lower station for the Wixi Skilift, is very easy walking, as it follows a farm track winding down the slope through rough pastures strewn with rocks and boulders. If you are going to stop and photograph the wonderful combinations of colourful plants growing among the rocks and boulders you will probably need to spend more than the 1 hour suggested! It is here that we have photographed *Anthyllis vulneraria* (common kidney-vetch), *Globularia nudicaulis* (leafless-stemmed globularia), *Polygala chamaebuxus* (shrubby milkwort) [Pl.16], *Sempervivum montanum* (mountain houseleek) [Pl.12] and *Veronica fruticans* (rock speedwell) [Pl.12].

Those who are prepared for much more strenuous walking could continue on past the Wixi Skilift to the top of a wooded slope where the path divides. Take the right-hand path which descends very steeply to the Biglenalp valley, where you can either take the path following the stream downwards to Mettlenalp and then take a path back to Wengernalp or cross the stream and walk over the next ridge, passing close by the alpine-dairy buildings and on through the conifer wood, to explore the remote pastures beyond, before making your way back to Wengernalp to rejoin the train to Kleine Scheidegg. Here you change trains to descend to Grindelwald, where you change again to go back to Interlaken Ost. If you are on a Regional Pass 'Free Day' you may like to take the train from Wengernalp back to Wengen and take the 10-minute walk through the traffic-free resort to the Männlichen cable-car for a speedy ride to the top of the mountain to enjoy the plants and scenery, (see Excursion 5) followed by a more gentle journey down on the gondelbahn to Grund and a short walk to the railway station for a train to Grindelwald, where you change train to return to Interlaken Ost.

E X C U R S I O N   8

STECHELBERG–TRACHSELLAUENEN

922m(3,025ft)-1,263m(4,144ft)

TRAIN:	Interlaken Ost to Lauterbrunnen	25min
POST-BUS:	Lauterbrunnen to Stechelberg	20min
WALK:	Stechelberg to Trachsellauenen and return	2-3hrs

Stechelberg is a small village at the end of the tarmac road to the upper part of the Lauterbrunnen valley (see p.57). Passengers for the hourly post-bus service from Lauterbrunnen are collected from the bus-stop just below the station entrance, on the opposite side of the road and can travel up the valley as far as the Stechelberg Hotel. From here there are various paths and tracks running up into the mountains and the large Nature Reserve. Continue up the valley through the village on foot, taking the Wanderweg on the eastern side of the fast flowing stream, the Weisse Lütschine. This twisting but easy path follows the stream up the valley, bordered, on one side, by high banks running up to the hay meadows, and by a downward-sloping boulder-strewn bank on the other side. As meadows are small and sloping you will probably be able to see traditional methods of hay-making using hand-tools and tripods for drying. Shrubs and small trees give some shade and provide a varied habitat for a wide range of herbaceous plants and ferns. We have found particularly good examples of larger plants here including *Aconitum vulparia* (wolfsbane) [P.14], *Astrantia major* (great masterwort) [Pl.14], *Cruciata laevipes* (crosswort), *Ligusticum mutellina* (alpine lovage) [Pl.13], *Rhinanthus minor* (yellow rattle), *Saxifraga rotundifolia* (round-leaved saxifrage), *Silene dioica* (red campion), *Silene nutans* (Nottingham catchfly), *Thalictrum aquilegifolium* (great meadow-rue) [Pl.14] and *Vincetoxicum hirundinaria* (sallow-wort). Shrubs in flower include *Berberis vulgaris* (barberry), *Rosa arvensis* (field rose) and *Rosa pendulina* (alpine rose). The ferns *Asplenium trichomanes* (maidenhair spleenwort) and *Asplenium viride* (green spleenwort) are well established among the boulders in the damp shady areas. The path becomes steeper after it crosses over a bridge to the west side of the stream in the small hamlet of Sichellauenen, altitude 1002m(3288ft). You then have the choice of continuing up the valley on the path to Trachselauenen or returning to Stechelberg on the path on the western side of the stream.

E X C U R S I O N   9

MÜRREN, ALLMENDHUBEL AND BLUMENTAL

1,645m △ (5,397ft), 1,934m △ (6,345ft), 1,852m △ (6,076ft)

TRAIN:	Interlaken Ost to Lauterbrunnen	25min
POST-BUS:	Lauterbrunnen to Stechelberg-Schilthornbahn	12min
CABLE-CAR:	Stechelberg to Gimmelwald	5min
CABLE-CAR:	Gimmelwald to Mürren	5min
WALK:	Mürren-Schilthornbahn to Mürren-Allmendhubelbahn	10min
FUNICULAR:	Mürren-Allmenhubelbahn to Allmendhubel	5min
WALK:	Allmendhubel to Mürren	1hr
TRAIN:	Mürren to Grütschalp	17min
FUNICULAR:	Grütschalp to Lauterbrunnen	9min
TRAIN:	Lauterbrunnen to Interlaken Ost	25min

Mürren is a popular ski-resort and holiday centre on a sunny terrace high above the Lauterbrunnen valley (see p.57). It has three stations, the middle station of the Schilthornbahn, the longest cable-way in the alps, the lower station of the Allmendhubel funicular, and the mountain-railway station for trains to and from Grütschalp, the top station of the funicular from Lauterbrunnen. Traditional chalets with attractive gardens, small shops, hotels and restaurants are surrounded by flower-filled meadows and pastures, with magnificent views of the Eiger, Mönch and Jungfrau. There is no access to the village by road and all visitors must either walk there, or use the Schilthornbahn cable-car from Stechelberg, or the funicular and mountain railway from Lauterbrunnen. On this excursion we suggest that you make a round trip by crossing over the road outside Lauterbrunnen station and walking a few yards downhill to the stop for the Stechelberg post-bus. Take the bus to the lower station of Schilthornbahn and then enjoy the spectacular cable-car journey to Gimmelwald. Here you change cable-cars without leaving the station and travel on to Mürren. If you do not wish to travel by cable-car you can reach Mürren by funicular and mountain-railway, full details in Excursion 10 (see p.65).

Gimmelwald, altitude 1,400m(4,593ft) is a very old settlement, dating back to 1330, and from here you can walk into the Sefinental, a remote valley which we have been told has many interesting plants. However it cannot be recommended as an 'easy-way' as the altitude at the bottom of the valley is 1,253m(4,111ft), over 480ft below Gimmelwald, and rises to 1,544m(5,066ft) at the head of the valley at Kilchbalm. Although we have visited Gimmelwald and walked a little way down the track towards the Sefinental we have not been able to explore this valley ourselves.

So on to Mürren by cable-car and then a 10-minute walk on more-or-less level ground, following the signs to the lower station of the Allmendhubel funicular for the short journey to the top of the mountain and into the alpine pastures where we have photographed *Arnica montana* (Arnica), *Bartsia alpina* (alpine bartsia), *Campanula barbata* [Pl.13], *Gentiana clusii* (Clusius's gentian). *Goodyera repens* (creeping lady's tresses), *Gymnadenia conopsea* (fragrant orchid) [Pl.7], two species of semi-parasitic plants *Pedicularis ascendens* (ascending lousewort) and *Pedicularis comosa* (crested lousewort), *Poa alpina* (alpine meadow grass) which produces young plantlets in place of flowers, *Pulsatilla alpina subsp. apiifolia* (yellow alpine pasque flower) [Pl.6], *Trifolium alpinum* (alpine clover) [Pl.9], *Veratrum album* (white false helleborine) and *Viola lutea* (mountain pansy). From Allmendhubel you can walk back to Mürren on easy downhill paths through the Blumental (the valley of flowers) or take a return trip on the funicular. To complete the expedition walk on through the village following the signs to the railway station to take the mountain-railway to Grütschalp where you will find that the platform for the funicular down to Lauterbrunnen opens off the railway platform. If you dislike looking out over a steep drop, concentrate on the plants on either side of the railway track, as you make a very steep descent into the Lauterbrunnen valley. From the bottom station of the funicular there is a pedestrian subway on to the platform where you take the train back to Interlaken Ost.

E X C U R S I O N 1 0

MÜRREN AND GRÜTSCHALP

1,645m Δ (5,397ft)-1,487m Δ (4,879ft)

TRAIN:	Interlaken Ost to Lauterbrunnen	25min
FUNICULAR:	Lauterbrunnen to Grütschalp	11min
TRAIN:	Grütschalp to Mürren	21min
WALK:	Mürren to Grütschalp	2hrs
FUNICULAR:	Grütschalp to Lauterbrunnen	11min
TRAIN:	Lauterbrunnen to Interlaken Ost	25min

For this excursion you travel to Mürren (see p.63) by funicular and train. The funicular station at Lauterbrunnen is opposite the railway station and there is a subway connecting the two stations, so there is no need to cross the busy road. Staff operating the funicular make sure that it is not overloaded by arranging for the number of passengers to fill one funicular to wait in a special enclosure. Once the maximum number of passengers permitted to travel on one journey has assembled, the gate is closed and is not re-opened until after the funicular has started on its journey to Grütschalp. The exit from the funicular at Grütschalp opens on to the platform for the mountain railway to Mürren. When you leave Mürren station, turn right and take the road following the railway line back towards Grütschalp. (Turn left if you wish to explore Mürren or use either the funicular to Allemendhubel or the Schilthornbahn.)

The official time for this gentle downhill walk is 1hr 10min but we usually take 2-3 hours, if the weather is good. There are ever changing views of the Jungfrau group and Schynige Platte as you walk along through a range of plant habitats containing a wide range of species. As you leave the village and take the track towards Grütschalp there is a high grassy bank on your left-hand side and if it has not yet been cut for hay you may be able to see *Acinos alpinus* (alpine calamint), *Anthyllis vulneraria* (common kidney-vetch), *Aster bellidiastrum* (false aster), *Campanula thyrsoides* (yellow bellflower) [Pl.8], *Dactylorhiza fuchsii*, *Helianthemum nummularium* (common rockrose), *Potentilla erecta* (tormentil), *Rumex acetosella* (sheep's sorrel) and many other meadow plants. The next section of the path runs along the edge of conifer forest and in the damper shady conditions you may see *Aconitum vulparia* (wolfsbane) [Pl.14], *Corallorhiza trifida* (coralroot orchid), the insectivorous plants, *Pinguicula alpina* (alpine butterwort) [Pl.15], and *Pinguicula vulgaris* (common butterwort), *Saxifraga rotundifolia* (round-leaved saxifrage), *Stellaria nemorum* (wood stitchwort), and *Viola biflora* (yellow wood violet). In sunny clearings and on rocky banks *Erinus alpinus* (fairy foxglove), *Polygala chamaebuxus* (shrubby milkwort) [Pl.16], *Silene vulgaris* (bladder campion), *Vaccinium vitis-idaea* (cowberry), *Veronica alpina* (alpine speedwell), and *Veronica fruticans* (rock speedwell) [Pl.12]. The path crosses several streams and boggy areas and here you may see *Caltha palustris* (marsh marigold) and *Orchis mascula* (early purple orchid). As you approach Winteregg station the trees thin and the path continues across rough grazing meadows with steep banks and outcrops of rock. *Carduus nutans* (musk thistle), *Carlina acaulis* (stemless carline thistle), *Cirsium spinosissimum* (spiniest thistle), *Crepis aurea* (golden hawksbeard) *Gymnadenia conopsea* (fragrant orchid) [Pl.7], *Phyteuma orbiculare* (round-headed rampion) [Pl.13], *Phyteuma scheuchzeri* (horned rampion), *Phyteuma spicatum* (spiked rampion), [Pl.13], *Platanthera bifolia* (lesser butterfly orchid), *Trifolium alpinum* (alpine clover) [Pl.9] and *Veratrum album* (white false helleborine) grow among the pasture grasses, and on the banks and among the boulders you may find *Campanula barbata* (bearded bellflower) [Pl.13], *Gypsophila repens* (alpine gypsophila), *Linaria alpina* (alpine toadflax) [Pl.11]. Near Grütschalp station there are more trees with dwarf shrubs and larger herbaceous plants growing among them including *Adenostyles alliariae* (adenostyles), *Aruncus dioicus* (goatsbeard spiraea), *Circaea lutetiana* (enchanter's nightshade), *Maianthemum bifolium* (May lily), *Melampyrum pratense* (common cow-wheat), *Rhododendron ferrugineum* (alpenrose) [Pl.16], *Rosa pendulina* (alpine rose) and *Vaccinium myrtillus* (bilberry)

[Pl.16]. When you reach Grütschalp take the funicular down to Lauterbrunnen and then a train back to Interlaken Ost.

E X C U R S I O N   1 1
ISENFLUH AND SULWALD

1,084m △ (3,557ft)-1,553m △ (5,030ft)

TRAIN:	Interlaken Ost to Lauterbrunnen	25min
POST-BUS:	Lauterbrunnen to Isenfluh	10min
CABLE-CAR:	Isenfluh to Sulwald	8min

Isenfluh is a small village high above the Lauterbrunnen valley (see p.57) which is accessible by post-bus from Lauterbrunnen station. From Isenfluh there are splendid views of Schynige Platte, the Männlichen, Eiger, Mönch and Jungfrau mountains. The cable-car takes you high up to Sulwald where there are small farms and traditional chalets scattered among wide hay-meadows and pastures filled with flowers. Up here there are well-maintained footpaths and tracks enabling you to enjoy the scenery and flowers very easily. If you walk northwards towards Interlaken and take the path through a patch of woodland you come to a clearing at the top of a steep cliff from where you can see Interlaken, backed by the Harder Kulm, lying between the Thunersee and Brienzersee. Under the trees of this wood we found *Aquilegia atrata* (dark columbine) and *Rhododendron ferrugineum* (alpenrose) [Pl.16] and *Heracleum austriacum* (Austrian hogweed). In the meadows we found particularly good plants of *Campanula rotundifolia* (harebell), *Centaurea alpina* (alpine knapweed) and *Onobrychis montana* (mountain sanfoin) among many other colourful flowers. Those who are prepared to walk uphill can continue upwards into the Sustal to the Suls-see or follow the Bergwege to Grütschalp and take the funicular back to Lauterbrunnen. Those needing an easy way must return to Lauterbrunnen the way they came, by cable-car and post-bus. However you may be surprised to find that passengers about to use the upper cable-car to descend to Isenfluh have to use the telephone at the upper station to alert the operators at the lower station that you wish to come down, you are then given full instructions for a do-it-yourself operation!

EXCURSIONS VIA SPIEZ   630m Δ (2,067ft)

TRAIN:	Interlaken Ost to Spiez	
	(Schnellzug)	20min
	(Regionalzug)	24min
or TRAIN:	Interlaken Ost to Interlaken West	3min
and BOAT:	Interlaken West to Speiz	1hr 25min

Spiez is a picturesque town, with many hotels and guest houses, built on a hillside running down to the southern shore of the Thunersee. Visitors from Interlaken can travel there by boat from Interlaken West, or by train from either Interlaken Ost or Interlaken West. The railway station and modern shopping centre are at the top of the slope, whilst the medieval castle stands in attractive gardens, overlooking the busy harbour for lake steamers, yachts and other small boats. The 11th century church adjoining the castle is used for concerts and recitals. A large vineyard covers the hillside to the north-west of the harbour. There is a regular bus service between the railway station and the harbour.

E X C U R S I O N 1 2 .

KIENTAL AND GRIESALP 906m Δ (2,973ft) & 1,407m Δ (4,616ft)

TRAIN:	Interlaken Ost to Spiez (Schnellzug)	20min
TRAIN:	Spiez to Reichenbach (Regionalzug)	8min
POST-BUS:	Reichenbach to Kiental	15min
(CHAIR-LIFT:	Kiental to Ramslauenen, walk & return	2hrs)
POST-BUS:	Kiental to Griesalp	25min

It is better to travel to Spiez by train on your way out so that you can catch a local train to Reichenbach easily by changing platforms at Spiez station. The Kiental post-bus leaves from the station and travels up the wooded valley to the village of the same name. When you reach the village you can either remain on the bus and continue up to Griesalp or stop to explore the village and its surroundings and if the weather is clear take the chair-lift up to Ramslauenen on the eastern side of the Gerihorn. The bus journey from Kiental to Griesalp is one you will never forget, the narrow road climbs steadily past the shallow Tschingel lake surrounded by wide marshes and then round a series of hairpin bends past the Pochten and Dünden falls. Above the village of Griesalp there is an area of forest with wide easy paths edged with rock-strewn banks making an ideal habitat for a range of colourful low-growing plants. In sunny clearings between the trees there are patches of *Acinos alpinus* (alpine calamint), and *Arctostaphylos uva-ursae* (bearberry), and in grassy areas *Phyteuma spp.* (rampions) are frequent, in damper areas *Geum rivale* (water avens), *Dactylorhiza fuchsii* (common spotted orchid) can be seen in large numbers whilst

Adenostyles alliariae and *Maianthemum bifolium* colonise the more shady areas. The post-bus will take you back to Reichenbach to catch a train back to Spiez to return to Interlaken by either train or by taking a more leisurely journey by boat. There is a pleasant 15min downhill walk from the railway station to the harbour through the castle gardens and overlooking the vineyard if you do not wish to wait for the next bus down to the quay.

EXCURSION 13

KANDERSTEG TO OESCHINEN

1,200m Δ (3,937ft)-1,700m Δ (5,578ft)

TRAIN:	Interlaken Ost to Spiez	20min
TRAIN:	Spiez to Kandersteg	28min
WALK:	to Oeschinen Sesselbahn	20min
CHAIR-LIFT:	Kandersteg to Oeschinen	7min

At Spiez (see p.69) change to a fast train that will take you on a fascinating journey up the Kander valley. Kandersteg is a popular summer and winter mountain resort which is over 500m(1,641ft) higher than Spiez; so the train has to zig-zag through a series of twisting tunnels cut deep into the rock walls of the valley as it approaches its destination. You will pass the same landmarks three times at different heights in the course of your journey, and even find yourself travelling back towards Spiez for a short distance! There are many hotels, guest-houses, shops and facilities for visitors in the long village set in a wide flower-filled valley enclosed by rugged mountains. Cars and lorries travelling by rail through the Lötschberg tunnel to the Rhone valley are loaded at the station.

When you leave Kandersteg railway station, follow the signs to the Sesselbahn, which will take you through the village and meadows on tarmac roads and level paths. There is an occasional local bus service between the railway station and the Oeschinen chair-lift. The chair lift seats passengers in pairs and you are carried silently 485m(1503ft) up the mountain, sitting side-by-side enjoying the plants and scenery, to the meadows at Oeschinen. There is a footpath, enabling you to climb to the same area, following the course of the Oeschibach, from Kandersteg to the Oeschinensee, where you then take a north-westerly path to the meadows. When you leave the chair-lift you will find all paths lead to the Oeschinensee, a beautiful deep blue lake, at the foot of the Blümlisalp mountain, which is popular with tourists and has appropriate facilities, restaurants, hotel, icecreams and paddle boats! But a leisurely walk across the meadows should enable you to see many attractive plants and to quietly enjoy the mountain scenery. Among the short grasses of the meadows near the cable-station there are *Alchemilla alpina* (alpine lady's mantle) [Pl.9], *Arenaria biflora* (two-flowered sandwort), *Centaurea montana* (mountain cornflower), *Euphorbia cyparissias* (Cypress spurge), *Galium helveticum* (Swiss bedstraw), *Gentiana acaulis* (trumpet gentian) [Pl.10], *Gentiana utriculosa* (bladder gentian), *Gentiana verna* (spring gentian) [Pl.10], *Gymnadenia albida* (small white orchid) [Pl.7], *Onobrychis montana* (mountain sanfoin), *Plantago media* (hoary plantain), *Primula farinosa* (birdseye primrose) [Pl.9], *Viola cenisia* (Mount Cenis pansy) and *Viola pyrenaica* (Pyrenean violet) among scores of other small herbaceous plants. In damp hollows there are *Anemone narcissiflora* (narcissus-flowered anemone) [Pl.15], *Orchis palustris* (bog orchid), *Pinguicula alpina* (alpine butterwort) [Pl.15] and *Soldanella alpina* (alpine snowbell) [Pl.5]. There are several rocky banks and screes where you can find *Acinos alpinus* (alpine calamint), *Dryas octopetala* (mountain avens) [Pl.11]. *Erinus alpinus* (fairy foxglove), *Globularia cordifolia* (matted globularia) [Pl.11], *Globularia nudicaulis* (leafless-stemmed globularia), *Polygala chamaebuxus* (shrubby milkwort) [Pl.16], *Potentilla crantzii* (alpine cinquefoil), and *Potentilla erecta* (tormentil). As you walk towards the Oeschinensee there are small groups of trees and bushes and here you may be lucky enough to find *Hepatica nobilis* (hepatica) growing with *Ranunculus montanus* (mountain buttercup) and with low shrubs such as *Daphne mezereum* (mezereon) and *Rubus caesius* (dewberry). A downhill walk through some denser woodland takes you to the shore of the lake 1,578m(5,177ft).

E X C U R S I O N   1 4

KANDERSTEG INTO THE GASTERNTAL

1,200m Δ (3,839ft)-1,590 Δ (5,217ft)

TRAIN:	Interlaken Ost to Spiez	20min
TRAIN:	Spiez to Kandersteg	28min
MINIBUS:	Kandersteg to Selden Hotel	25min

Selden is a tiny hamlet at the foot of the mountains at the top of the Gasterntal [Pl.1]. There is an infrequent minibus service with a regular timetable from Kandersteg station, and it is best to book a seat by telephoning Th.Schmid 033/ 71 11 71, the day before you wish to go. Make sure that arrangements are made for your return trip in the minibus. The road into the valley is very narrow, single-track in some sections, passing through several tunnels and a deep gorge. Selden is surrounded by meadows and pastures lying between the high mountain walls and the river Kander. There are Bergwege leading up to the Hockenhorn, Balmhorn and Doldenhorn but we have spent several hours exploring the meadows using the footbridges to cross and recross the river. On the banks of the river you can find high mountain plants such as *Campanula pulla* (solitary harebell), *Epilobium fleischeri* (alpine willowherb), *Erinus alpinus* (fairy foxglove), *Gypsophila repens* (alpine gypsophila), *Saxifraga aizoides* (yellow mountain saxifrage) [Pl.15], *Saxifraga paniculata* (paniculate saxifrage) and *Veronica aphylla* (leafless-stemmed veronica) [Pl.4], that have become established on the wide scree banks having been thrown down with stones and boulders eroded from higher levels. Among the trees and shrubs bordering the river there are *Corallorhiza trifida* (coralroot orchid), *Moneses uniflora* (one-flowered wintergreen) and *Pyrola minor* (common wintergreen). At the sunny edge of the trees bordering the stream there are well developed plants of *Echium vulgare* (viper's bugloss), *Gentiana lutea* (great yellow gentian), *Geranium endressii* (western cranesbill), *Lilium martagon* (martagon lily) [Pl.13] and *Vaccinium vitis-idaea* (cowberry) [Pl.16]. In the hay meadows there are fine specimens of *Onobrychis montana* (mountain sanfoin), *Phyteuma nigrum* (black rampion) and *Phyteuma orbiculare* (round-headed rampion) [Pl.13].

E X C U R S I O N 1 5

KANDERSTEG TO SUNNBÜEL

1,200m Δ (3,839ft)-1,930m Δ (4,595ft)

TRAIN:	Interlaken Ost to Spiez	20min
TRAIN:	Spiez to Kandersteg	28min
LOCAL BUS:	Kandersteg station to Stock Talstation	10min
CABLE-CAR:	Stock to Sunnbüel	7min

Sunnbüel is one of the best places we know to see early flowering alpine plants in the wild, provided that you go at the right time, for that particular season, and the weather is good. It is not worth attempting this excursion if clouds are low over the mountains. When you leave Kandersteg railway station (see p.72) take the local bus from the station-yard to Stock. Tourist half-price and 'free day' concessions are not available on this service. The alternative is a long uphill walk southwards through the village and the upper meadows to Stock, taking us at least 40min. The cable-car will then take you quickly to the high alpine pastures. Here there are large areas of short grasses interspersed with carpets of low-growing plants including *Alchemilla alpina* (alpine lady's mantle) [Pl.9], *Alyssoides utriculata* (alyssoides), *Anthyllis vulneraria var. alpestris* (alpine kidney-vetch), *Bartsia alpina* (alpine bartsia), *Gentiana verna* (spring gentian) [Pl.10], *Myosotis alpina* (alpine forget-me-not), *Pedicularis verticillata* (verticillate lousewort) [Pl.8], *Primula farinosa* (Birdseye primrose) [Pl.9], *Pulsatilla alpina* (alpine pasque flower) [Pl.6] and *Silene acaulis* (moss campion) [Pl.12]. On rocky outcrops there are mats of *Dryas octopetala* (mountain avens) [Pl.11], *Globularia cordifolia* (matted globularia) [Pl.11], *Globularia nudicaulis* (leafless-stemmed globularia),

Helianthemum spp. (rockroses), *Polygala chamaebuxus* (shrubby milkwort) [Pl.16], *Ranunculus alpestris* (alpine buttercup), *Salix reticulata* (netted willow) [Pl.16], *Salix retusa* (blunt-leaved willow), *Salix serpyllifolia* (thyme-leaved willow) and *Viola biflora* (yellow wood violet) [Pl.4]. In damp shady hollows there are patches of *Saxifraga rotundifolia* (round-leaved saxifrage) and *Thalictrum macrocarpum* (large-fruited meadow-rue). As you walk southwards across the Spitalmatte towards the small Arvenseeli lake, 1,889m(4,498ft) the pastures are lusher and you can see *Gymnadenia conopsea* (fragrant orchid) [Pl.7], *Onobrychis arenaria* (small sanfoin), and *Platanthera bifolia* (lesser butterfly orchid) [Pl.7].

Those able to walk comfortably at these altitudes can continue on the undulating Wanderweg past the Arvenseeli for about 1¹/₂hrs to the Daubensee, 2,205m(7,235ft), and from there for a further 1¹/₂hrs to the Gemmipass, 2,316m(7,599ft).

However, there is a fairly easy downhill track from the upper cable-car station at Sunnbüel taking you through an area of rather broken ground where you can find a range of shade-loving plants growing in damper conditions between the rocks and boulders amongst stunted trees and bushes on the upper edge of the tree-line. *Anemone narcissiflora* (narcissus-flowered anemone) [Pl.15], *Dactylorhiza incarnata* (early marsh orchid), *Geum rivale* (water avens), *Lonicera alpigena* (alpine honeysuckle), *Oxalis acetosella* (wood-sorrel), *Pinguicula alpina* (alpine butterwort) [Pl.15], *Primula auricula* (auricula) [Pl.3], *Primula elatior* (oxlip), *Ranunculus nemorosus* (wood buttercup), *Sagina saginoides* (alpine pearlwort), *Thalictrum aquilegifolium* (great meadow-rue) [Pl.14], *Trollius europaeus* (globeflower) [Pl.15], *Valeriana tripteris* (three-leaved valerian) and *Veratrum album* (white false helleborine).

The path from here back to Kandersteg is very steep and we recommend that you take one of the paths back to the upper cable-station for an easy descent.

E X C U R S I O N 1 6	
FAFLERALP	**1,788m Δ (5,866ft)**

TRAIN:	Interlaken Ost to Spiez (Schnellzug)	20min
TRAIN:	Spiez to Goppenstein	42min
POST-BUS:	Goppenstein to Fafleralp	35min

Many, but not quite all, of the trains from Spiez (see p.69) running through the Lötschberg tunnel to Brig, in the Rhône valley, stop at Goppenstein, so check carefully when you change trains at Spiez. Fafleralp lies at the top of the remote Lötschental valley which only became easily accessible to tourists in 1910, with the opening of the Lötschberg railway. Centuries of isolation have preserved many ancient customs and traditions, making visitors from the Bernese Oberland feel that they are entering a different world. The post-bus starts from outside Goppenstein railway station and travels up the valley to Fafleralp, stopping on its way, at Ferden, Kippel, Wiler, Reid and Blatten. Many of the low rather dark-coloured wooden houses display grotesque masks which are used at carnival time. At the head of the valley there are wide mountain pastures criss-crossed by fast-flowing streams running down from the glaciers and screes.

The pastures contain numerous attractive plants, including a large number of *Paradisia liliastrum* (St.Bruno's lily) [Pl.13] with *Astragalus depressus* (sprawling milk-vetch),

Campanula persicifolia (peach-leaved bellflower), *Campanula rapunculoides* (creeping bellflower), *Campanula rotundifolia* (harebell), *Gentianella amarella* (felwort), *Geranium pyrenaicum* (Pyrenean cranesbill), *Geranium sylvaticum* (wood cranesbill), *Phyteuma hemisphaerica* (globe-headed rampion), *Phyteuma scorzonerifolium* (scorzonera-leaved rampion), *Silene nutans* (Nottingham catchfly), *Silene vulgaris* (bladder campion), *Trifolium alpinum* (alpine clover) [Pl.9] and *Veratrum album* (white false helleborine). Among the shorter grasses near the screes and among the rocks on the banks of the streams *Campanula barbata* (bearded bellflower) [Pl.13], *Gentiana bavarica* (Bavarian gentian), *Hieracium alpinum* (alpine hawkweed), *Pedicularis tuberosa* (long-beaked lousewort), *Potentilla rupestris* (rock cinquefoil), *Rumex acetosella* (sheep's sorrel), *Sempervivum montanum* (mountain houseleek) [Pl.12] and *Veronica alpina* (alpine speedwell) can be found.

Those wishing to explore paths at a higher level can take the cable-car from Wiler, 1,421m(4,662ft), for the 4 minute journey to Lauchernalp, 1,970m(6,464ft). Here there is a network of paths through high meadows, eastwards to Fafleralp, or westwards to Ferden.

E X C U R S I O N   1 7

RIEDERALP AND HOHFLUH

1,930m Δ (6,332ft) and 2,227 Δ (7,307ft)

TRAIN:	Interlaken Ost to Spiez (Schnellzug)	20min
TRAIN:	Spiez to Brig (Schnellzug)	58min
TRAIN:	Brig to Mörel	12min
CABLE-CAR:	Mörel to Riederalp	15min
WALK:	south-west through village	10min
CHAIR-LIFT:	Riederalp to Hohfluh	10min

This excursion takes you through the Lötschberg tunnel into the Rhône valley by express train from Spiez (see p.69) to Brig. At Brig you leave the main-line station and take a local train which runs on an open track, rather like a tram-way, through the station forecourt, and then keeps close to the river as it makes its way up the valley to Mörel, giving passengers wide views of the river and the mountains towards Italy. At Mörel, 759m(2,490ft), you leave the train and take the cable-car through Greich to the ski-resort at Riederalp. Here you follow the signs through the village, on paths beside the flower-filled meadows surrounding the hotels and guest-houses, to the Sesselbahn for the final stage to Hohfluh. A short walk across rough hummocky pasture takes you to a view-point overlooking the Aletschgletscher which flows slowly down from the Jungfrau. In these high pastures we have seen a number of plants that we have not seen in the wild on any of our other excursions. These include *Cardamine plumieri* (ivy-leaved bittercress), *Dactylorhiza sambucina* (elder-flowered orchid) [Pl.6], *Gentiana alpina* (southern gentian), *Ranunculus glacialis* (glacier crowfoot) [Pl.4], *Ranunculus pyrenaeus* (Pyrenean buttercup) and *Veronica bellidioides* (violet speedwell). We also photographed *Androsace obtusifolia* (blunt-leaved rock-jasmine), *Crocus albiflorus* (white crocus), *Gentiana clusii* (Clusius's gentian), *Geum montanum* (alpine avens), *Loiseleuria procumbens* (creeping azalea) [Pl.16], *Polygala chamaebuxus* (shrubby milkwort) [Pl.16], *Pulsatilla vernalis* (spring pasque flower) [Pl.6] and *Viola calcarata* (long-spurred pansy).

From the top station of the chair-lift there are footpaths which we cannot describe as easy ways, either following the ridge overlooking the glacier westwards to the Aletsch Nature Centre or eastwards past the Blausee and the Bettmersee to Bettmeralp, 1,950m(6,398ft) from where you can take a cable-car down to Betten FO, 758m(2,487ft) to catch a train back to Brig or take the gondelbahn up the Bettmerhorn, 2,867m(9,407ft).

E X C U R S I O N   1 8

ENGSTLIGENALP 1,941m △ (6,368ft)

TRAIN:	Interlaken Ost to Spiez (Schnellzug)	20min
TRAIN:	Spiez to Frutigen	11min
BUS:	Frutigen to Adelboden-Oey	22min
BUS:	Adelboden-Oey to Unter dem Birg	12min
CABLE-CAR:	Unter dem Birg to Engstligenalp	4min

From Spiez (see p.69) take a train to Frutigen where you will find buses for Adelboden waiting outside the station. When you buy your ticket explain to the driver that you are heading for Engstligenalp and need to change buses at Adelboden-Oey which is a small village on the outskirts of Adelboden. When you are set down at Adelboden-Oey, cross over the road, walk a very short distance towards Adelboden, (the same direction as the bus you have just got off) and take the first turning on your left and wait on the bus stop a few yards down the hill on the right-hand side. A bus from Adelboden will then take you on to the cable-car station at Unter dem Birg. The cable-car takes you up to a wide expanse of rather marshy cattle pastures, strewn with boulders and rocks, and crossed by numerous fast flowing streams. We have only made one visit here but we shall certainly go back again and hope for better weather. In the short time before the mist and cloud descended we found sheets of *Pinguicula alpina* (alpine butterwort) [Pl.15], *Plantago alpina* (alpine plantain), *Primula elatior* (oxlip), and *Primula farinosa* (birdseye primrose) [Pl.9] among the pasture grasses. Among the rocks and boulders we found *Dryas octopetala* [Pl.11], *Gentiana verna* (spring gentian) [Pl.10], *Globularia cordifolia* [Pl.11], *Salix serpyllifolia* (thyme-leaved willow) and *Silene acaulis* (moss campion) [Pl.12].

E X C U R S I O N 1 9

THE NIESEN KULM   2,362m Δ (7,750ft)

TRAIN:	Interlaken Ost to Spiez (Schnellzug)	20min
TRAIN:	Spiez to Mülenen (Regionalzug)	6min
FUNICULAR:	Mülenen to Schwandegg	14min
FUNICULAR:	Schwandegg to Niesen Kulm	12min

This is an excursion where you can reach a considerable height very easily and in good weather you should be able to have panoramic views of both Brienzersee and Thunersee as well as the Kandertal and Simmental. There is also an amazing range of plants growing around the summit of this conical mountain in very bleak conditions. This is an excursion where you need to take that extra pullover particularly if you make your visit on a sunless morning, but you will also need your sun-hat when the clouds lift! The train for Mülenen leaves Spiez (see p.69) station from the Kandersteg platform, but be careful that you are taking a local train that will be stopping there. When you leave Mülenen station, cross the road to the lower station for the Niesen Bahn for the funicular to Schwandegg. When you reach this intermediate stop you walk across the terraced station to another funicular waiting to take you up to the top station, which is near the hotel, a few metres below the summit. As soon as you leave the station buildings you can see the zig-zag footpath up the mountain and the system of snow-fences which protect the cableway. It is not an easy walk down the mountain and we strongly advise you to return to the valley by the funicular, after you have climbed the short distance to the viewing area where there is a telescope, and sign-boards giving the names of the surrounding mountains. Among the rocks on either side of the path to the summit we have photographed *Androsace spp.* (rock-jasmines), *Astragalus australis* (southern milk-vetch), *Astragalus glycophyllus* (wild liquorice), *Bartsia alpina* (alpine bartsia), *Carlina acaulis* (stemless carline thistle), *Carum carvi* (caraway), *Doronicum columnae* (heart-leaved leopardsbane), *Hedysarum hedysaroides* (alpine sanfoin), *Hutchinsia alpina* (Chamois cress) [Pl.12], *Ligusticum mutellina* (alpine lovage) [Pl.13], *Lloydia serotina* (Snowdon Lily) *Pedicularis verticillata* (verticillate lousewort) [Pl.8] and *Silene acaulis* (moss campion), [Pl.12]. It is often very windy up here and it is not easy to get close to the plants so not many of our photographs are suitable for publication! If you find that when you return to the valley you have time to spare before a train is due to take you back to Spiez there is a pleasant path along the bank of the Kander river.

E X C U R S I O N   2 0

GRIMMIALP   1,222m △ (4,009ft)

TRAIN:	Interlaken Ost to Spiez (Schnellzug)	20min
TRAIN:	Spiez to Oey-Diemtigen (Regionalzug)	12min
POST-BUS:	Oey-Diemtigen to Grimmialp, Hotel Spillgerten	35min

At Spiez (see p.69) change on to the Zweisimmen line but be sure to take a local train that will stop at Oey. The post-bus leaves from outside the station and will take you up the Diemtigtal through attractive villages and hay-meadows to Grimmialp. Here there are many footpaths to choose from. We followed the path alongside the Senggibach stream to a small lake, the Blauseeli which is bordered by shady trees. Among these trees we found *Lilium martagon* (martagon lily), *Epipactis atrorubens* (dark red helleborine), *Saxifraga aizoides* (yellow mountain saxifrage) and *Tofieldia calyculata* (Tofield's asphodel). We then walked on into alpine pastures containing a wide range of herbaceous plants and including *Astrantia major* (great masterwort) [Pl.14], and *Campanula glomerata* (clustered bellflower) that were considerably smaller than those we are accustomed to seeing in UK gardens. Among the meadow plants we also found *Gypsophila repens* which was rather taller than plants growing in UK gardens, and also *Linum catharticum* (purging flax), many *Phyteuma spp.* (rampions) and *Orchis ustulata* (burnt orchid) [Pl.7]. There is much to see here in very peaceful surroundings before making your return journey by post-bus and train to Spiez.

E X C U R S I O N   2 1

CHATEAUX D'OEX AND LA BRAYE

958m Δ (3,143ft) and 1,625m Δ (5,332ft)

TRAIN:	Interlaken Ost to Spiez (Schnellzug)	20min
TRAIN:	Spiez to Zweisimmen (Schnellzug)	36min
TRAIN:	Zweisimmen to Châteaux-d'Oex	50min
CABLE-CAR:	Châteaux-d'Oex to La Braye	18min

This excursion takes you by train from Spiez (see p.69), through the Simmental to Saanenland where the train negotiates a series of dramatic curves as it approaches Gstaad at the western end of the Bernese Oberland. From here you continue towards Montreux to Châteaux-d'Oex which lies in the deep valley of the Sarine river, in the Pays d'Enhaut of the French-speaking canton of Vaud. An hourly cable-car service from Châteaux-d'Oex to La Braye takes you high above the village to alpine pastures with numerous attractive plants including some of the more unusual orchid species. In one short visit in very poor weather we were able to find *Coeloglossum viride* (frog orchid), *Dactylorhiza fuchsii* (common spotted orchid) *Gentiana lutea* (great yellow gentian), *Nigritella nigra* (black vanilla orchid), *Orchis ustulata* (burnt orchid) [Pl.7], *Platanthera bifolia* (lesser butterfly orchid) [Pl.7], *Tofieldia calyculata* (Tofield's asphodel) and *Traunsteinera globosa* (round-headed orchid), before increasing cloud and rain forced us to go back down to the valley.

EXCURSION 22

THE STOCKHORN AND CHRINDI

2,190m Δ (7,185ft) and 1,640m Δ (5,381ft)

TRAIN:	Interlaken Ost to Spiez (Schnellzug)	20min
TRAIN:	Spiez to Erlenbach	15mins
CABLE-CAR:	Erlenbach to Stockhorn (via Chrindi)	15mins

As on Excursion 20 (see p.83) take a local train on the Zweisimmen line, this time to Erlenbach. When you leave the station walk through the village until you reach the main road, then turn west towards Boltigen and you will find the lower station of the Stockhornbahn on the right-hand side of the road. The same cable-car will take you through the intermediate station at Chrindi and on up nearly to the summit of the mountain. Behind the restaurant there is a short steep path up to the summit where you will be rewarded with a wonderful view of the surrounding mountains. There are several information panels giving the names and heights of all the peaks you can see from special viewing points. The plants growing along the edge of this path have been carefully labelled and include *Daphne mezereum* (mezereon), *Helianthemum oelandicum subsp. alpestre* (alpine rockrose), *Hutchinsia alpina* (Chamois cress) [Pl.12], *Myosotis alpestris* (alpine wood forget-me-not), *Petrocallis pyrenaica* (Pyrenean whitlow-grass), *Saxifraga moschata* (musky saxifrage) and *Silene acaulis* (moss campion) [Pl.12]. The path is steep but there are steps and hand-rails to help you on your way and it really is worth the effort of walking uphill at this altitude! On your downward trip break your journey at Chrindi. Here there is a wide choice of walks at a lower altitude and a restaurant near the cable-station. The cable-car crosses the Hinterstocken lake as you approach Chrindi from the top station. The lake is encircled by an easy undulating path with interesting plants on either side. Along the lakeside there are some marshy areas where *Ranunculus aconitifolius* grows in large drifts. On the slightly drier areas on the other side of the path *Primula farinosa* (birdseye primrose) [Pl.9], *Ranunculus polyanthemos* (multiflowered buttercup), *Stachys palustris* (marsh woundwort), *Stellaria holostea* (greater stitchwort), *Vicia sepium* (bush vetch) and *Viola lutea* (mountain pansy) are well established. At the southwest side of the lake there are rocky outcrops and substantial cliffs and here *Globularia cordifolia* (matted globularia) and *Saxifraga paniculata* (paniculate saxifrage) grow in the crevices of the rocks whilst *Soldanella alpina* (alpine snowbell) [Pl.5] grows in shady damp hollows where snow has melted only recently. A westerly path over a low ridge takes you to another lake, the Oberstockensee 1,665m(5,463ft) but we have not walked there ourselves.

EXCURSIONS FROM INTERLAKEN   567m Δ (1,890ft)

A description of Interlaken has been included in Chapter 2 (see p.5). Interlaken became the tourist centre for the Bernese Oberland during the 19th Century when many hotels and shops were established to accommodate Victorian travellers from Britain and other parts of Europe. There is a magnificent view of the Jungfrau from the large meadow adjoining the main street in the centre of the town.

Full details of travel facilities can be found in Chapter 2, page 5.

Primula farinosa
– birdseye primrose

Lloydia serotina
– Snowdon lily

(above) Alchemilla alpina
– alpine lady's mantle

(below) Trifolium alpinum
– alpine clover

Plate 9

Gentiana punctata
– spotted gentian

Gentiana brachyphylla
– short-leaved gentian

Gentiana verna
– spring gentian

Gentiana acaulis
– trumpet gentian

Plate 10

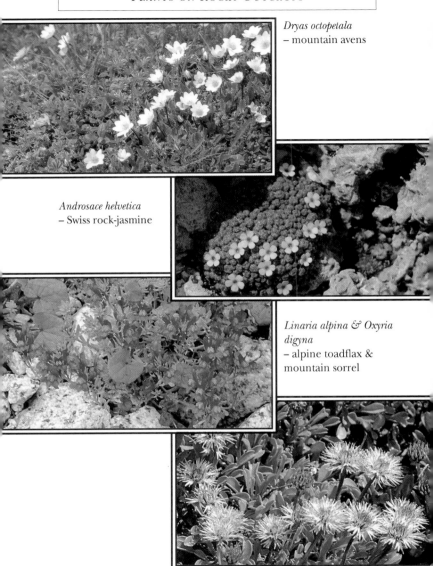

Dryas octopetala
– mountain avens

Androsace helvetica
– Swiss rock-jasmine

Linaria alpina & Oxyria digyna
– alpine toadflax &
mountain sorrel

Globularia cordifolia
– matted globularia

Plate 11

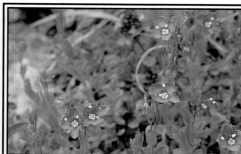

Veronica fruticans – rock speedwell

Sempervivum montanum
– mountain houseleek

Silene acaulis
– moss campion

Hutchinsia alpina – Chamois cress

Plate 12

(right) Paradisea liliastrum – St Bruno's lily

(left) Lilium martagon – Martagon lily

(right) Phyteuma orbiculare – round-headed rampion

(left) Campanula barbata – bearded bellflower

(right) Meadow plants including *Ligusticum mutellina, Geranium spp., Leucanthemum vulgare* – alpine lovage, cranesbill and ox-eye daisy

(left) Phyteuma spicatum – spiked rampion

Plate 13

Aconitum vulparia – wolfsbane

Astrantia major – great masterwort

Swertia perennis – marsh felwort

Thalictrum aquilegifolium – great meadow-rue

Plate 14

PLANTS GROWING IN DAMP CONDITIONS

Trollius europaeus
– globeflower

Anemone narcissiflora
– narcissus-flowered anemone

Pinguicula alpina
– alpine butterwort

Gagea fistulosa
– gagea

(left) Cypripedium calceolus
– lady's slipper orchid

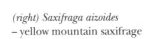

(right) Saxifraga aizoides
– yellow mountain saxifrage

Plate 15

(left) Loiseluria procumbens &
Vaccinium myrtillus – creeping azalea
& bilberry or whortleberry

(below) Rhododendron ferrugineum
– alpenrose

(below) Vaccinium myrtillus
– bilberry or whortleberry

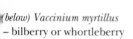

(below) Salix reticulata – netted willow

(right) Polygala chamaebuxus
– shrubby milkwort

(left) Clematis alpina – alpine clematis

Plate 16

E X C U R S I O N   2 3

__NIEDERHORN__   1,950m Δ (6,398ft)

POST-BUS:	Interlaken West to Beatenberg Sesselbahn	30min
CHAIR-LIFT:	Beatenberg to Niederhorn	18min
WALK:		
CHAIR-LIFT:	Niederhorn to Beatenberg	18min
WALK:	Beatenberg Sesselbahn to Beatenberg Funicular	20min
FUNICULAR:	Beatenberg to Beatenbucht	10min
BUS:	Beatenbucht to Oberhofen	18min
BUS:	Oberhofen to Interlaken West	45min
or BOAT:	Oberhofen to Interlaken West	1hr 45min

On this excursion you will travel into the mountains for a walk with superb views and interesting plants and then use a variety of forms of transport to visit a historical museum in an ancient lakeside castle. The post-bus for Beatenberg, 1,146m(3,760ft), starts from outside Interlaken West Station taking a narrow winding route through wooded country to a sunny terrace above the Thunersee to what is said to be the 'longest village in Switzerland'. Be patient, you will eventually reach the chair-lift which carries passengers in pairs, side-by-side, to the summit of the Niederhorn. Here there are wide views over the Thunersee to Spiez and the mountains on either side of the Kander valley. Cattle graze within a few yards of the chair-lift and the restaurant but there are plenty of small colourful flowers among the short turf protected by the fences which keep both tourists and animals from the edge of the steep cliffs bordering the Justistal to the north-west of the mountain. *Androsace chamaejasme* (ciliate rock-jasmine), and *Androsace obtusifolia* (blunt-leaved rock-jasmine), *Helianthemum nummularium*, *Poa alpina* (alpine meadow grass), *Polygonum viviparum* (alpine bistort) and *Thymus serpyllum* (wild thyme) flourish here, well out of reach of those rasping tongues.

From the Niederhorn there are paths along the ridge towards Gemmenalp, 2,067m(6,782ft) and then downhill to Waldegg or Habkern, but these are not easy ways and we must take the chair-lift down again to Beatenberg. A 20 minute walk westwards, along a level road, brings you to the upper station of the funicular which runs down to the edge of the Thunersee. A half-hourly bus service will take you along the lake shore to Oberhofen, where the 12th-century castle, with many 19th-century additions, is used as a branch of the Bernese Historical Museum. The castle is set in attractive lakeside gardens with many shrubs and trees as well an elaborate scheme of colourful formal beds. From here you can return to Interlaken by bus or boat.

E X C U R S I O N   2 4

HABKERN TAL   1,055m Δ (3,461ft)

POST-BUS: Interlaken West to Habkern   20min

This excursion takes you through Unterseen, the old village adjoining Interlaken, on the north bank of the river Aare, on through the lower part of the Habkern valley to the village of the same name. You will pass farms with relatively large fields where modern machinery can be used for hay-making. When you reach the bus terminus at the post office take the road up the gently sloping valley through carefully tended meadows. On the banks on either side of the road you may see *Arnica montana* (arnica), *Astragalus depressus* (sprawling milk-vetch), *Euphrasia rostkoviana* (common eyebright) and *Trifolium montanum* (mountain clover). After walking through a small area of woodland you will reach a damp marshy area where you may find *Dactylorhiza fuchsii* (common spotted orchid), *Dactylorhiza majalis* (broad-leaved marsh orchid) [Pl.6], *Lychnis flos-cuculi* (ragged robin), Orchis ustulata (burnt orchid) [Pl.7], *Platanthera bifolia* (lesser butterfly orchid) and *Swertia perennis* (marsh felwort) [Pl.14].

EXCURSION FROM BRIENZ   567m Δ (1,860ft)

Brienz, the centre of the Bernese Oberland wood-carving industry, with a wood-carving school and many workshops, is an ancient town running along the north-eastern shore of the Brienzersee. The carved wooden houses of the Brunnergasse are decorated with flower-filled window-boxes during the summer months, and every visitor takes home a treasured photograph from here! Behind the attractive lakeside town, with its many hotels and guesthouses, the wooded slopes rise steeply to the Brienzer Rothorn. A bus from outside the railway station takes you to the Swiss Open Air Museum of Rural Life at Ballenberg, where traditional buildings are used to illustrate the crafts and customs of the rural areas. The buildings have been moved from sites throughout Switzerland and have been rebuilt in 124 acres of wooded grounds. Many of the buildings are furnished and are used for craft demonstrations.

E X C U R S I O N   2 5

ROTHORN KULM AND PLANALP

2,350m Δ (7,710ft) and 1,344m Δ (4,410ft)

TRAIN:	Interlaken Ost to Brienz	16min
TRAIN:	Brienz to Rothorn Kulm	50min
TRAIN:	Rothorn Kulm to Planalp	34min
WALK:		1-2hr
TRAIN:	Planalp to Brienz	25min
BOAT:	Brienz to Interlaken Ost	1hr 15min

Cross over the main street outside Brienz railway station to the lower station for the Brienzer Rothorn Bahn for a fascinating journey up the mountain. Some of the trains are still pulled by steam locomotives, but others have more modern diesel engines. The railway track winds up through the village, to the woods and forest and then out above the tree-line above Planalp, to wind round a dramatic rocky coombe, giving passengers superb views over the Brienzersee to the mountains beyond. The train travels very slowly giving ample opportunities to enjoy the meadow flowers on either side of the track. The train takes you to within a few yards of the rugged summit where a few plants can be found in crevices in the rocks by the side of the path to the hotel. Wind, and often clouds and mist, make photography difficult up here, but this is where we took our only photograph of *Draba fladnizensis* (bald white whitlow-grass). If you walk on past the hotel you come to the upper station for the cable-car running down to Schönenboden in the Mariental, but those needing an easy way should take the Brienzer Rothorn Bahn back to the rural hamlet of Planalp to explore the fairly level paths through the lower pastures where we have found *Alchemilla vulgaris* (lady's mantle), *Aquilegia atrata* (dark columbine), *Aster bellidiastrum* (false aster), *Campanula barbata* (bearded bellflower) [Pl.13], *Carduus carlinifolius* (carline-leaved thistle), *Epilobium alpestre* (whorled-leaved willowherb), *Epilobium montanum* (mountain willowherb), *Erinus alpinus* (fairy foxglove), *Filipendula ulmaria* (meadowsweet) *Galium helveticum* (swiss bedstraw), *Geranium pratense* (meadow cranesbill), *Geum rivale* (water avens), *Knautia dipsacifolia* (wood scabious), *Lilium martagon* (martagon lily) [Pl.13], *Lysimachia nemorum* (yellow pimpernel), *Phyteuma spicatum* (spiked rampion) [Pl.13], *Platanthera bifolia* (lesser butterfly orchid) [Pl.7], *Poa alpina* (alpine meadow grass), *Polygala serpyllifolia* (thyme-leaved milkwort), *Polygonum bistorta* (bistort), *Potentilla erecta* (tormentil), *Prunella grandiflora* (larger self-heal), *Ranunculus aconitifolius* (aconite-leaved buttercup), *Rosa pendulina* (alpine rose), *Stachys sylvatica* (hedge woundwort) and *Thalictrum aquilegifolium* [Pl.14]. After returning to Brienz by train, we hope you will have sufficient time to make the journey back to Interlaken by the boat which takes you past the spectacular waterfall at Giessbach, to the village of Iseltwald and on to Bönigen before tying up at the quay adjoining Interlaken Ost station. There is a shady lake-side footpath from Giessbach through Iseltwald to Bönigen, perhaps not one of the best places for seeing wild plants but nevertheless a very pleasant undulating walk. Bönigen, 569m(1,867ft) is a peaceful village with beautiful carved houses with attractive painted frescos, some dating from 1549. It has excellent facilities for visitors but still retains a true village atmosphere with a lively community engaged in local activities. Until a few years ago there was no road to Iseltwald, and the boat service was the only means of transport for visitors and the local community.

EXCURSION FROM MEIRINGEN   600m Δ (1,969ft)

TRAIN: Interlaken Ost to Meiringen   28min

Meiringen lies in the Hasli valley to the east of the
Brienzersee. It is a good tourist centre near to the Aare
Gorge and the Reichenbach Falls (see p.53).

E X C U R S I O N   2 6
ENGSTLENALP   1,834m Δ (6,017ft)

TRAIN: Interlaken Ost to Meiringen   28min
POST-BUS: Meiringen to Engstlenalp   55min

The post-bus for Engstlenalp leaves from Meiringen
station but it is wise to go to the post-bus office opposite
the station to book a return ticket to and from Engstlenalp
as soon as you arrive in Meiringen. Extra buses are often
provided, if it is known that many people are hoping to
travel. The post-bus goes first to Innertkirchen
625m(2051ft) and then turns into the Gental. This is a
beautiful wooded valley, gently sloping at first, but
becoming steeper and steeper as the narrow road, with
frequent hair-pin bends, takes you up into the mountains.
There is a very small hamlet at Engstlenalp, one hotel and
a few farms, surrounded by rough pastures which run
down to the shores of the Engstlensee. There are good
paths across the rather shrubby pastures on fairly level
ground, making it easy to move around to look for the
varied selection of plants that grow on this somewhat
windswept alp. *Alchemilla alpina* (alpine lady's mantle)

[Pl.9], *Arctostaphylos uva-ursi* (bearberry), *Bartsia alpina* (alpine bartsia), *Daphne mezereum* (mezereon), *Euphorbia cyparissias* (Cypress spurge), *Gagea fistulosa* (yellow gagea) [Pl.15], *Gentiana acaulis* (trumpet gentian) [Pl.10], *Gentiana verna* (spring gentian) [Pl.10], *Geum montanum* (alpine avens), *Globularia cordifolia* (matted globularia) [Pl.11], *Gymnadenia conopsea* (fragrant orchid) [Pl.7], *Hieracium aurantiacum* (orange hawkweed), *Homogyne alpina* (alpine coltsfoot) [Pl.8], *Myosotis alpestris* (alpine wood forget-me-not), *Myosotis alpina* (alpine forget-me-not), *Oxalis acetosella* (wood-sorrel), *Pinguicula alpina* (alpine butterwort) [Pl.15], *Polygala chamaebuxus* (shrubby milkwort) [Pl.16], *Potentilla crantzii* (alpine cinquefoil), *Primula elatior* (oxlip), *Primula farinosa* (birdseye primrose) [Pl.9]. *Rhinanthus minor* (yellow rattle), *Rhododendron ferrugineum* (alpenrose) [Pl.16], *Silene acaulis* (moss campion) [Pl.12], *Soldanella pusilla* (least snowbell) [Pl.5], *Trifolium alpinum* (alpine clover), [Pl.9] and *Vaccinium myrtillus* (bilberry) [Pl.16]. Those well able to walk uphill at this altitude may wish to take the path around the northern side of the lake and take the chair-lift to the Joch pass, 2,207m(7,241ft).

Index

TRAVEL VOCABULARY

GERMAN	ENGLISH
Abfahrt	departure time
Ankunft	arrival time
Ausgang	exit
Bach	stream
Bahn	railway
Bahnhof	railway station
Bergfahrt	upward journey
Bergweg	mountain path
Billett	ticket
Eingang	entrance
Fahrplan	timetable
Gleis	platform or track
Gondelbahn	gondola railway
Halt auf Verlangen	request stop
Haltestelle	bus stop
letzte	last
Luftseilbahn	cable-car
Minute	minute
Regionalzug	local train
Rückfahrkarte	return ticket
Panoramaweg	path with view
Preis	price
Rauchen verboten	no smoking
Schiff	boat
Schiffstation	quay
Schnellzug	express train
See	lake
Seilbahn	funicular
Sesselbahn	chair-lift
Stunde	hour
Tal	valley
Talfahrt	downward journey
Wanderweg	footpath

ENGLISH	GERMAN
arrival time	Ankunft
boat	Schiff
bus stop	Haltestelle
cable-car	Luftseilbahn
chair-lift	Sesselbahn
departure time	Abfahrt
downward journey	Talfahrt
entrance	Eingang
exit	Ausgang
express train	Schnellzug
footpath	Wanderweg
funicular	Seilbahn
gondola railway	Gondelbahn
hour	Stunde
lake	See
last	letzte
local train	Regionalzug
minute	Minute
mountain path	Bergwege
no smoking	Rauchen verboten
platform	Gleis
price	Preis
quay	Schiffstation
railway	Bahn
railway station	Bahnhof
request stop	Halt auf Verlangen
return ticket	Rückfahrkarte
stream	Bach
ticket	Billett
timetable	Fahrplan
track	Gleis
upward journey	Bergfahrt
valley	Tal